W9-CHS-099

APOLLO
on the
MOON

APOLLO on the MOON

by
Henry S. F. Cooper, Jr.

The Dial Press, Inc.
New York 1969

Copyright © 1969 by Henry S. F. Cooper, Jr.

The material in this book appeared originally in *The New Yorker* magazine in a slightly different form. The author wishes to thank Mr. Charles Patrick Crow and Mr. Robert Daniel Menaker for their help in preparing the manuscript —and in particular to thank Mr. William Shawn for making the book possible in the first place.

All rights reserved. No part of this book may be reproduced in any form or by any means without the prior written permission of the Publisher, excepting brief quotes used in connection with reviews written specifically for inclusion in a magazine or newspaper.

Library of Congress Catalog Card Number: 70-84940

Design by Thomas Clemens

Printed in the United States of America

First printing, 1969

To Mary and Elizabeth

Table of Contents

Author's Note

Even though most of the attention centering around the Apollo Project has focussed on the rockets and spacecraft that will land two men on the moon, a number of people at the National Aeronautics and Space Administration have been concentrating on what the astronauts will do once they are there. This book tries to set down the procedures that the astronauts will follow during their first few visits on the moon, together with some of their purposes in being there—as well as to give some idea of what it is like to *be* on the moon. It is the account of a plan and should be read in the manner of someone reading the script of a play, complete with descriptions of scenery and instructions, before he goes to see it—or, as people do sometimes, *after* he has seen it. The play may have four productions in the next year or so. There are bound to be changes in the script, not to mention improvisations by the actors themselves, so it may be useful for comparison to have an idea of the original concept.

New York, N.Y.
March, 1969

PART I
Landing

On warm, hazy evenings, the moon sometimes appears to be soft and yellow, and sometimes swollen and orange, but on clear, crisp nights, when the moon is full, it shines so harshly against the black sky that it can hurt the eyes. On these nights, the moon is small, precise, and round, like a smooth glass marble that is mottled with splotches of black, gray, and white. This summer, two astronauts will probably land on a patch of black that is near the middle of the side of the moon that always faces the earth. The white areas are craggy highlands, and anybody on earth with a pair of binoculars can see that setting a rocket ship down there would be a tricky operation. The blacker parts, called *maria,* because astronomers used to think they were seas, are lowlands that look smooth and level—and, indeed, are. The two astronauts will arrive in a lunar module, or LM, which will have carried them down from the Apollo spacecraft proper. (The National Aeronautics and Space Administration has never been good at naming spacecraft or anything else—a failing it first demonstrated when it named the project to go to the moon after the god of the sun.) The flight down to the moon will be only the third time an LM will have been flown by astronauts; the first time was during the Apollo 9 mission in March, when it was flown in orbit around the earth, and the second in May, on the Apollo 10 mission, in orbit around the moon. During the landing, now scheduled for Apollo 11 this summer, the Apollo command module itself will stay in orbit sixty-nine miles above the moon, and in it will be a third astronaut, who may be able to follow the LM with his eyes all the way to the lunar ground. From that height, according to the Apollo 8 astronauts who orbited the moon last December, the lunar surface is "a vastness of black and white" that looks like "dirty beach sand with lots of footprints in it." To the astronaut left behind in the Apollo spacecraft, the LM will look like a delicate firefly, occasionally flashing orange as its rocket blasts to slow it. In fact, everything about the LM—it is black and bronze with splashes of silver, like certain bees—is buglike, though different parts look as if they came from different bugs. The astronauts call it "Spider," and indeed the four long, spindly legs are like spiders', though the feet, round dishes, are like water skates'. On top, there is a welter of antennas. The design of the LM is as difficult to make out as the jumbled anatomy of a mosquito because it flies only in space and therefore it needn't be designed aerodynamically; the astronauts think of it as the first true manned spacecraft.

The trip down will take about an hour, during which time the LM will travel a gradual descent path halfway around the moon, moving from the dark side to the light. Inside, the cockpit is lit softly like an airliner's. The LM pilot stands on the right and the LM commander (who will do most of the piloting—another NASA misnomer) stands on the left. They are standing because there are no seats in the LM; seats had been included in the original plans, but as the flight down is so short, the astronauts will hardly need chairs to rest in. They will be too busy flying the spacecraft to sit down. After the LM moves away from the command module—it will do so with short bursts from small rockets used for making minor adjustments in the LM's position—the commander will fire the big descent rocket to slow the craft from its orbital speed of thirty-five hundred miles an hour and put it into a trajectory path that astronauts call a Hohmann descent transfer orbit. The astronauts will have to keep a close watch on their Hohmann descent transfer orbit, and all other orbits, for the moon's interior may be lumpy, instead of having a uniform core like the earth, and the lumpiness may cause an unevenness in the moon's gravitational field which in turn could make the LM wander off its predicted path. To check their path, they will make frequent plots of their position with the Alignment Optical Telescope, which is overhead between the two astronauts and which they handle like a sextant, getting fixes on a number of stars and also on some landmarks below on the moon. They won't lack for landmarks, for as they sweep around from the dark side of the moon to the light, they may notice, as did two astronauts in a book written by H. G. Wells in 1901, "The First Men in the Moon," that "the whole area [of the spaceship's window] was moon, a stupendous scimitar of white dawn with its edges hacked out by notches of darkness . . . out of which peaks and pinnacles came climbing into the blaze of the sun." As the astronauts get fixes on the peaks and pinnacles (actually, the moon is a good deal flatter than Wells thought it was) they will check any incipient feelings of vertigo by frequent references to an instrument they call the eightball, which is a free-floating ball set into the dashboard in front of each astronaut; it is marked with longitudinal and latitudinal lines, like a terrestrial globe, and acts a little like a carpenter's level by showing when the spacecraft is upright—in relation to the horizon. Hundreds of knobs, buttons, and dials threaten the astronauts from all sides; the

LM's numerous dashboards and control panels would win no prizes for safety of design, even in Detroit. One control that the astronauts will be careful not to hit accidentally is a prominent black-and-yellow button ominously labeled "ABORT"; when it is pressed, the lower stage of the LM, with the descent rocket, drops off; and the ascent rocket fires to send the upper stage, and the astronauts, hurtling back to the Apollo command module. In case of an emergency, even an accidental one, a guidance computer located behind the LM's commander would automatically guide what was left of the LM back to its rendezvous. The automatic-guidance system could also land the LM at its target on the moon, but the astronauts will in all probability want to take it in all the way by hand. When the LM is about fifty thousand feet above the moon and some two hundred and twenty-five miles from its landing site, the commander will fire the descent rocket a second time to brake at full thrust, putting the spacecraft into a steeper descent orbit, which will take it down to ten thousand feet. The descent engine will then blast a third time, putting the LM into a third descent orbit, which should bring it down to seven hundred feet, within view of the landing site. All this time, of course, the LM is traveling horizontally as well as vertically. The target the astronauts are aiming for is an imaginary oval about five miles long and three miles broad.

For the first landings, NASA has picked out five sites along the moon's equator; the astronauts may very likely land at the one to the left of center, Site 4, which is the second most westerly of the five. As they are all very similar, one would do as well as another. The landing has been timed for twenty-four hours after dawn, when the sun's rays will rake across the landing site, throwing it into relief. It takes two weeks for the sun to move across the sky. The sites are far enough apart so that one target would be in early morning sunlight at any time during the several days of a launch period at Cape Kennedy. Site 4, which would be the third target, is near the eastern edge of the Oceanus Procellarum, an irregular *mare* that is darker than most and is so vast that it runs from close to the center of the moon to the western edge. At about one hundred feet, the LM, its descent rocket pointing directly down toward the moon, will descend vertically at about three feet a second, as if it were a spider dropping straight down from the sky on a single strand of web. It will ride down slowly on the flaming jet of the rocket. The commander will keep one hand on a throttle that adjusts the rocket's blast and the other on a lever that controls roll, pitch, and yaw. The astronauts may think they are descending faster than they actually are, for, the moon being smaller than the earth, objects disappear faster over the horizon. As they come down, the morning sun will be catching the western rims of the thousands of small craters that pit Site 4. The two triangular windows they are looking through, each two layers of high-strength glass, are slanted inward at the bottom to give them a better view straight down. The astronauts may pull the shades on the windows down part way in order to avoid what they call sunshafting—blinding sunlight streaming into a spacecraft's cockpit, which is a danger during landing because the sun is so low on the horizon. The commander may throttle down the rocket so that the LM is hovering; and as the rocket tilts this way and that like an outboard motor, he can select the best spot to come down on. He will do his best to avoid boulders, craters, and side hills. When one or another of the four landing probes, which are about five feet long and serve much the same purpose as the feelers of an insect, touch the ground, a blue indicator on the dashboard, called the moon contact light, turns on; the pilot shuts off the rocket; and the LM drops the rest of the way, landing (the astronauts hope) with a jolt thought to be no more than that of a three-foot jump on earth, perhaps less if they land in soft, loose material—the reason for the feet ending in round dishes. As the legs telescope down (they are stuffed with a sort of honeycomb material made of aluminum that compresses to absorb the shock), the astronauts may settle onto the moon as gently as a moth.

After landing, the astronauts can get on with the job they came close to a quarter of a million miles to do. Just getting acclimated might be work enough for the first trip, because the moon is a queer place to be, with its gravity one-sixth the earth's, so that at first the astronauts may flounder and bounce about like men learning to use a trampoline. The moon is a dangerous place, too, for it is a near vacuum, and it is bombarded with intense radiation; the temperature there can drop to two hundred and fifty degrees below zero and rise to two hundred and thirty degrees above. In spite of all these discomforts, however, the astronauts will have to busy themselves getting the answers to a long list of questions about the moon. The questions, formulated by a committee of NASA scientists, are so basic that they would do equally well for astronauts going to another planet. Among them are: Does the moon have a hot, liquid core like the earth? Are there volcanoes on the moon, and does the ground occasionally tremble with a moonquake? What are the rocks made of? What forces dug the craters? How were the *maria* leveled so neatly? Is there life on the moon? How *old* is the moon, and where did it come from?

Those first two astronauts will have to hustle, and so will the pairs of astronauts to come after them, because the accumulated time that all the Apollo astronauts will have on the moon is hardly enough to find out everything the scientists want to know. Though NASA wants at least ten Apollo landings on the moon, only four attempts are definite, beginning possibly with Apollo 11 this summer. If all goes well with that one, it will be followed, at approximately two-and-a-half month intervals, by Apollos 12, 13, and 14. Even ten landings would be hardly enough to explore in much detail a land the size of Africa. Each visit will be short, because the LM is equipped to be on the moon for only about twenty-four hours—forty-eight hours at the most. The astronauts won't have anything like that amount of time for exploration, though. They can leave the LM for about three hours at a stretch, because their portable life-support systems have to be small enough to be carried on their backs. Indeed, the first astronauts on the moon will leave the spacecraft for just *one* three-hour period. Because the time spent on the moon will be so short, priorities have to be figured carefully. During the first landing, the astronauts will gather samples of rock and dirt within a hundred feet of where they land, for bringing back samples of the moon is the highest priority of all. They may also deposit a couple of extremely simple scientific instruments on the moon, and then, if there is any time left, they may take a short walk—not more than a few hundred feet—picking up any interesting-looking rocks that catch their eye.

The astronauts on the second trip and later ones will gather more samples, and they will also set about the second order of business, which is to lay out a number of scientific instruments, such as a seismometer, to record moonquakes, and a magnetometer, to measure the moon's magnetic field, if it has one. Then the astronauts will climb back into their spacecraft and may try to snatch a few hours' sleep. If they go outside for another three hours, as they are expected to do on all missions after the first, they will go on a long field trip, during which they may walk as far as a mile, taking snapshots and occasionally picking up a chunk of rock, which they will carefully describe and catalogue before squirreling it away in a sack. On the field trip, they could turn up almost anything. One thing they could find is traces of the earliest forms of life on earth, all evidence of which has long since been obliterated here by lava flows but vestiges of which might have been preserved in the vacuum-packed, freeze-dried environment of the moon. Many scientists, among them the chemist Dr. Harold C. Urey, of the University of California, feel that life might have reached the moon along with a big splash of water when the moon was first caught in the earth's gravity—an event that these scientists postulate as having happened over four billion years ago. Under this theory, the moon may then have come close to (or even collided with) the earth, causing immense tidal waves, which could have showered the moon with water and protozoa. Recently, Dr. Urey, whom selenologists consider their elder statesman, said, "I so hope the early history of the moon hasn't been obliterated with lava, the way it has been here. I hope the astronauts will find material preserved from the early days of the solar system." Each of the astronauts now in training for the moon landings hopes to be one of those who will make the field trip. They all look forward to it more than to any other part of their visit—not only because of the chance of finding Dr. Urey's protozoa but more especially because it will give them the best opportunity to see what they can *do* on the moon; after all, finding out how men perform in an alien environment is essential for all exploration of the moon and the planets. Accordingly, outfitting the astronauts with just the right equipment for use on the moon has become a major part of the space industry.

By the time the astronauts step onto the moon, it will have taken some twenty-four billion dollars, and the work of some twenty thousand corporations, to get them there. The space industry—it is equivalent to the industrial effort for a small war—is spread all across the country. Many of the big aircraft companies that are the prime contractors for spacecraft and rockets are on the West Coast, but the LM comes from the Grumman Aircraft Engineering Corporation, at Bethpage, Long Island—a thirty minute drive from Manhattan. The site of the Grumman plant is almost as bleak and dismal as the surface of the moon. Several dozen buildings resembling oversized barracks are scattered around a vast asphalt parking lot that looks blasted and flattened like the inside of a huge crater. Approximately ten thousand cars, which in the setting seem like lumpy lunar boulders, stretch to a horizon traced in the distance by a fine silvery line—a steam pipe running above the ground for more than a mile, as if it were the crater's rim. Plant No. 5, where the LM's are assembled, is a sprawling, shapeless structure surmounted by what appears to be a dull-blue moon but is in fact a radar dome. Inside Plant No. 5 is a huge white room the size of an airplane hangar, called the clean room, where the LM's are put together. (NASA has ordered fifteen, at a cost of over one and one-half billion dollars.) Overhead, a yellow crane rides back and forth along tracks on the ceiling. Below, stretching in two rows down the length of the room, are as many as eight white metal scaffolds that surround the LM's so completely that about all that can be seen of them is an occasional round, silvery fuel tank or some black antennas. A long spidery leg might be leaning against a beam, as though the place were some sort of Brobdingnagian entomologist's laboratory. On shelves, an LM's aluminum skin—it is only four one-thousandths of an inch thick—is stacked up like sections of a beetle's shell. Technicians, looking like laboratory assistants in white nylon smocks, swarm over the scaffolds, each one containing either an upper or lower stage of a LM. The technicians wear different-colored hats—red for the men working on the propulsion systems, green for environmental-control systems, yellow for avionics and instrumentation, and several other colors, too. Like lab assistants, they have delicate tasks to perform, and accordingly they wear gloves and sometimes even face masks. Inside the scaffolds, the LM's equipment bays are uncovered like open incisions, revealing floods of golden wire cascading in bewildering tangles. Outside, at the base of each scaffold, are the framed photographs of the astronauts and the back-up astronauts who are assigned to fly the LM inside; the technicians, amid all the black boxes and floods of wire, are never allowed to forget that they are responsible for two men's lives.

The men who are going to the moon come from an entirely different place—for one thing, it is a good deal better looking on the outside than Grumman. Both what the astronauts are going to do on the moon and what they will do it with are being planned at the Manned Spacecraft Center, which covers sixteen hundred acres of flat, scrubby land on a Texas plain midway between Houston and Galveston. (This isn't the first recorded connection between would-be moon explorers and that Texas plain. A century ago, the astronauts in Jules Verne's "From the Earth to the Moon" considered a plain near Galveston as a potential site for the cannon that was to shoot them to the moon. Oddly, Verne's astronauts finally settled on Florida for the launching site, just as NASA has.) Unlike Grumman, the Manned Spacecraft Center resembles a college campus, consisting, as it does, of an enormous grassy quadrangle rimmed by a number of airy white buildings, many with columns making them look like modern versions of Greek temples. At one end of the lawn is the administration building, a tall, antiseptic structure that dominates the other buildings, which are low and sprawling; halfway down the lawn is a squat, square building that looks as if it housed classrooms, and indeed, it may be said to do so, for it is where the astronauts have their offices; and across the lawn from the astronauts is a chunky building without windows—the Mission Control Center, which is the command headquarters for the trip. It has no windows lest a hurricane strike the space center while the astronauts are on the moon and wreck all the control equipment. Most of the men at the M.S.C. are tanned and athletic-looking, and most have their hair cut very short; that is to say, most of them look the way college students looked a decade ago, which is when most of them graduated. In a way, the M.S.C. is a college, but a college with a faculty and administration of about five thousand and a student body of only fifty-two—the astronauts. It takes at least three years to prepare a man to go to the moon. The astronauts must all pick up the equivalent of master's degrees in astronomy, physics, and geology. (Geology, not astronomy, may turn out to be the most useful science on the moon, for, as one astronaut says, "the moon is just one big rock pile.") They have to know how to fly jet planes, which are the closest thing around to spacecraft, and they have to learn to be spacecraft mechanics—a skill that may ultimately determine whether they get back home. People who have taught the astronauts never cease to marvel at the facility with which they pick up new information, the reason for the facility being that the astronauts are what they call "a highly motivated group," the motivation deriving from the desire not to miss out on any information that could be essential later, and so the astronauts cram in their astronomy, physics, geology, and spaceship mechanics as carefully as if they were storing data in computers—and that is pretty much the way they regard their training.

If the M.S.C. looks like a university, it also resembles a modern electronics firm, and in fact many of the electronics companies, such as General Electric, have enormous buildings, in matching architecture, on its fringes. In many ways, preparing astronauts isn't much different from building LM's. To get used to being on the moon, the astronauts are toasted at high temperatures, spun in centrifuges, and dunked in water to produce an effect of weightlessness, just as the electronic components of the LM are tested before being installed. The LM is full of small black boxes that contain components of its electrical system; if the electronics in one black box prove defective, the box can be yanked out quickly and replaced with another. The same is true of the astronauts, any one of whom can be yanked out of the master plan for going to the moon and replaced with another. Indeed, one astronaut, in explaining why the United States was sending men instead of more and better unmanned craft, went as far as to say that "a man, with his brains, is the cheapest computer equipment that NASA can send to the moon." A group of engineers called human-factors engineers have had as much to do as anybody else with making the astronauts seem like black boxes, for it is their job to treat the men as if they were components of mechanical or electronic systems; to them astronauts and spaceship are parts of one machine for getting to the moon, the astronauts being an integral part of the circuitry in that they complete the "control loop."

The astronauts are so much a part of the circuitry that

they haven't the slightest doubt about whether the United States should be going to the moon in the first place. Rather, they—and everyone else at the space center—take the position that America has already made the decision to be what one engineer there calls "a space-faring nation," and that, this decision having been made, there is no point in thinking about it further. The people at the space center get upset when anybody does think further. They give short shrift to the argument that the United States should not spend billions on being a space-faring nation when people in the country are starving. One of the few selenologists who do attempt to deal with this question is Dr. Urey; he has said that he has occasional twinges of guilt for fear the gigantic effort to put two men on the moon may be similar to building the Pyramids—another national effort that involved a prodigious outlay of funds for reasons that included vanity, and that came close to bankrupting a country. These twinges are transitory, however. Dr. Urey has explained, "Perhaps the nation will gain in self-respect from completing the Apollo Project, which in turn might make Americans more interested in tackling other big projects, like the urban areas and the poor. We can afford all this, and Apollo, too." He feels that if there were no Apollo Project, there is no reason to think that funds would be diverted to the war on poverty; things being the way they are in Washington, the money would doubtless find its way into almost everything else. "If there had never been any Apollo Project, cars would be a foot longer," Dr. Urey grumbles. At the M.S.C., one of the few people who think of the space program's influence on earth is an astronaut,

Don Lind, who gives the impression of being somewhat more thoughtful than many of his colleagues. Lind, who is a Mormon, says he likes to think of the trip to the moon as a possible alternative to war, especially as a stimulus to new technology. He says, "You can get the same technological advances that you do in wartime, only without killing people. It's a nicer way of stimulating people in laboratories to do their best." Neither Lind nor anyone else at NASA seems to have developed the idea of space exploration as an alternative to war any further than thinking it might be "a nicer way of stimulating people in laboratories." Nobody there seems particularly interested in the idea—expressed most recently by Anthony Storr, the British psychiatrist and author of the book "Human Aggression"—that the space race is a subconscious ritualization of war, in the same way that the rituals of most animals are substitutes for hostile combat against their own species. If so, the space race would be worth every cent spent upon it. Far from worrying about the social implications of going to the moon, most of the astronauts and virtually all the other people at the M.S.C. regard themselves as working toward a highly desirable goal. What that goal is, exactly, they find hard to put into words. Dr. Marcus G. Langseth, a geologist at the Lamont-Doherty Geological Observatory, just up the Hudson from New York City, who is designing a drill the astronauts will use to bore two holes in the moon, has given this question some thought without arriving at any answer he can regard as satisfactory. He says, tentatively, "Everyone under forty has grown up with the assumption that we *would* go to the moon someday. When I was at school, in the nineteen-forties, mathematical problems often went something like 'If a train takes four days to go from New York to San Francisco, how many days will it take to go to the moon?' " In Dr. Langseth's view, going to the moon is an impulse ingrained in the national character, as though Americans were astronautical lemmings. This vague feeling that the moon is pulling more toward it than just the tides is at the root of a great deal of NASA thinking. Some men, like Dr. Wilmot Hess, a tall, blond physicist, who is director of science and applications for the M.S.C., are outraged at the thought that we might *not* go to the moon, though Dr. Hess, too, is hard-pressed to say precisely why we *are* going. Dr. Hess, who has been called NASA's resident philosopher, resorts to what he calls the categorical imperative. The categorical imperative, as Dr. Hess uses it, is the same argument that mountaineers have used to justify climbing Mount Everest. "We're going to the moon because it's *there*," Dr. Hess says firmly. "Imagine yourself twenty years from now, and put yourself in the position of our *not* having gone to the moon. It's unthinkable!" People at NASA don't like to talk much about twenty years from now, partly out of fear that there may be nothing to talk *about*, if Congress continues to cut the space budget, and partly out of a fear of being thought too visionary, for every NASA man nourishes a secret hope that twenty years from now there will be colonies on the moon, and astronauts will be zooming off to the planets. NASA men, a hardheaded bunch, have a perpetual fear of being thought too visionary, yet they obviously have these thoughts at the backs of their minds. After all, the moon is, as Arthur C. Clarke once wrote, man's "first bridgehead in space." Much of Clarke's science fiction, like the film "2001," is based on the idea that man's destiny must somehow be worked out among the stars—a notion that Clarke spells out none too clearly and that the men at the space center don't spell out at all. Nevertheless, the notion may be part of what keeps them all going.

It is a good bet that when the first men step onto the moon, they won't be worrying about whether they should be there, unless they're beginning to wish they had never left home. If they want to beat a hasty retreat, they can do so two minutes after they have landed, when the Apollo spacecraft overhead will be in a good position for a rendezvous with the LM. If they decide to stay, their first job will be to run through most of the countdown for takeoff, to make sure they *can* get away—a job that one NASA engineer has defined as being "a morale-building exercise." At the moment, the last thing most of the men at the M.S.C. need is morale building. They have been so saturated with details about the visit to the moon, and they believe so intently in its coming to pass, that they can describe it as minutely as if it had already happened. For example, they tell you that the first man to stand on the moon will leave the LM through its forward hatch feet first and on his stomach, for after a lot of practice at the M.S.C. the astronauts have found that way to be the best. He will back across a sort of bridge—which the astronauts call the front porch—that leads to the top of the ladder that runs down one leg. The material that covers the bridge has been tested against the material on the soles of the astronauts' boots to prevent slipping. The astronaut could, of course, jump from the hatch to the lunar surface —a distance of eleven feet, which is a small hop on the moon—but he might fall and rip his space suit on a rock. As the suit is inflated with pure oxygen (as is the LM's cabin when it is pressurized), ripping is a major concern, and accordingly the hatch, the bridge, the ladder, and all other equipment that the astronauts are likely to go near are as smooth as possible. Everything has been designed especially for use on the moon; so much metal has been pared from the ladder, to save weight on the trip up, that on earth it would collapse under the weight of a man. Nothing of the sort will happen on the moon, where the astronaut is one-sixth his normal weight, but even so, as arrivals go, that of the first astronaut on the moon will be an awkward one. To reach the ground, this astronaut probably will not *climb* down the LM's ladder, for the astronauts, in their clumsy space suits, have found it easier to sort of *slither* down it instead. On his way down, the astronaut will have to flick a lever that will open a couple of baggage compartments at the back of the LM. At the bottom, he will lower himself very cautiously onto the ground. Therefore, man's first physical contact with the moon will be made neither with the left foot nor with the right, but probably with both feet together. His arrival on the moon will be recorded on film by the astronaut inside the LM. He will be very much relieved if he finds that the moon doesn't swallow him up like quicksand, for although there is good reason to believe that it won't, he can't be absolutely sure until he is there. In all likelihood, his boots will sink into the lunar surface about one-quarter of an inch, since the ground on most of the moon is thought to have the consistency of wet beach sand. His feet will probably not scuff up small wisps of dust when they hit the ground, because the dusty material, though certainly not wet, is slightly cohesive. One Midwestern geologist has likened it to loamy Iowa soil. Whether the surface is most like sand, dust, loam, or even powder, its particles are much finer than the sand on a beach, and much darker. The first crater that the astronaut will see as he steadies himself by grasping the ladder and looks down at his feet will be a shallow, man-made one, carved out by the LM rocket's exhaust; it will be approximately fifteen feet across and a foot deep. The rocket blast will have helped sweep the landing place clean. The ground around the astronauts will have been smooth to begin with, even by the billiard-table standards of *maria,* because for the landing NASA will try to avoid areas with craters more than two feet deep or rocks more than two feet high, to keep the LM from landing tilted. The five Apollo sites were chosen with safety very much in mind, for, as Lind says, "the first few times, we want to make darn sure we get there and back without busting our tails." If the LM tilts more than thirty degrees, it will have trouble taking off again, because the telescope for the guidance system would be pointing below the horizon. (No matter what angle the LM is tilted at, though, the astronauts will *try* to take off.) Consequently, all five Apollo sites are flat, like asphalt parking lots, except that they are pocked with small craters and littered with a loose, rocky rubble. Assuming that the astronauts have landed at the center of Site 4, at the eastern edge of the Oceanus Procellarum, they won't see a single hill or a distant mountain peak; mountains, which might interfere with the LM's flight path, have been avoided. The nearest mountains are fifty kilometres away, out of sight over the steep curvature of the moon. (The metric system is used on the moon, because inches, feet, and yards—Anglo-Saxon measurements based on the human body—are too provincial for general use in the solar system.) For a six-foot (that is, about two-metre) astronaut, the horizon will be only a couple of kilometres (that is, less than a mile and a half) away; it will surround him with the precision of a circle drawn by a compass on a piece of black paper.

The chances are that the astronaut—assuming the moon hasn't swallowed him up—will be excited, and, accordingly, the planners, who try to be on top of everything, have virtually programmed in a few moments of enthusiasm. "Can you imagine stepping onto the moon and *not* being excited?" says Lind, who is something of a romantic among astronauts, and who, as a child, may have done some of the same mathematical problems that fascinated Dr. Langseth. Lind and another astronaut, Harrison Schmitt, are the first ones to be assigned to work with the equipment that will be used on the moon. Though Lind and Schmitt will almost certainly not be the first astronauts to land on the moon, they are sure that they will get there. Lind rushes on glowingly, "Was Marco Polo excited when he got to Cathay? Was Columbus excited when he discovered America? Was Captain Cooke excited when he reached Australia? I can't imagine landing on the moon without letting out a whoop." Any such whoop will be inaudible on the moon, because sound doesn't travel in a vacuum. It will, however, be audible by radio to the other astronaut, who will still be inside the LM, waiting to make sure that nothing untoward befalls the first astronaut before he emerges himself (it is possible that on the first trip one astronaut will remain inside the LM all the time), and it will also be audible at the Mission Operations Control Room in Houston, a room illuminated only by an eerie white light. The flight director and other technicians will be sitting, in an expectant hush, at four banks of desks that face several big screens, on which teletype messages and maps of the landing area are flashed. Space technicians are mostly lean, trim, scrubbed-looking men with crew cuts, who look as if they had been stripped down, mentally and physically, to perform their jobs more efficiently, the way racing cars are stripped of their fenders to make them go faster. In the Mission Operations Control Room, which is kept fairly dark so that the technicians will be able to read the information on the electronic screens, the conversation, clipped and harsh sounding, will be mostly in numbers and acronyms, symbols unintelligible to outsiders. Most of the technicians are in their twenties or early thirties. On a bulletin board near the Mission Control Center there is an advertisement reading, "HELP WANTED: Prefer Veteran, with M.A. Degree and Ten Years' Experience. Age to 25," which, if it is a joke, comes very close to the truth. Chris Kraft, who was the flight director of the earlier Mercury and Gemini flights, is considered the grandfather of the flight-control technicians. He is forty-five. Glynn Lunney, who was the flight director for the Apollo 7 flight last October, and who may well be the flight director for the moon landings, is thirty-one.

It will take one and three-tenths seconds for the astronaut's whoop to reach the Mission Control Center, and another one and three-tenths seconds for an answering shout to reach the astronauts on the moon, and by the time these two and six-tenths seconds have elapsed, the astronaut who whooped may have begun to have some second thoughts. Indeed, both astronauts may have begun to feel that their original enthusiasm was misguided, for a lunar *mare,* a dead place, is no beauty spot. At the M.S.C. there is a mockup of the landing site—a four-acre slag heap pitted with gaping craters and dotted with jagged rocks. A recent visitor found that its nicest feature was the green grass beyond its fringes—an adornment that the real article will lack. Men feel uncomfortable in the absence of other life, much as they do when they look over the edge of a precipice. The astronaut may suddenly feel lonely and exposed, for although the horizon is only a couple of kilometres away, he won't feel snugly surrounded by the Lilliputian countryside. On the contrary, he will feel small and unreal, for, with virtually nothing in the landscape that he can relate to, it will be as though he were in a featureless round room painted gray-black. His depth perception will play tricks on him, making it even harder for him to come to terms with the landscape, for there is no darkening with distance, as there is on earth, where the color scale provided by the atmosphere is a great help in judging distances. The only colors the astronaut will see on the moon will be the ones he brought with him—primarily the red, white, and blue of two American flags, one of which will be sewn on his space suit and the other painted on the side of the LM, itself a mixture of black, bronze, and silver. Everything else will be colorless and unfamiliar. Like the blackish ground, the sky will be black—far blacker than the gound, though, since the astronauts will be looking straight at the emptiness of space. If he cups his hands over his eyes, he may be able to see stars, even though the sun is up. The shadows around him will be much inkier than they are on earth, and they will be long, for the sun will be hovering only about twelve degrees above the horizon; nonetheless, the temperature will already have reached about a hundred and thirty degrees above zero and be rising steadily. (At sunup about twenty-four hours before, the temperature will have shot up some two hundred degrees—from two hundred and thirty degrees below zero to only thirty degrees below zero—in twenty minutes, for heat travels quickly in a vacuum.) Even the sun will be strange to the astronauts—concentrated to the size of a dime and blazing many times as brightly as it does on earth. The only familiar object in view beyond the LM will be the earth itself, a hazy blue ball near the zenith, but since few men will have seen it quite this way before, it may be the most disconcerting object of all.

The astronauts won't have much time to feel uncomfortable, however; they will be far too busy running errands for scientists back on earth. "We will be representing the entire scientific community," Lind said recently. Lind and Schmitt differ about how much the first astronauts will be able to tell the scientific community about the moon during their first moments there. Schmitt, who was a geologist before he became an astronaut, says that, scientifically, the first look around will not tell him more than he already knows from the Surveyor photographs, but Lind says that the astronauts will be gathering new impressions from the instant they land. "We'll learn by just *being* there!" Lind says. In Lind's case, the initial whoop of excitement may take a long time to wear off. He adds, "Just by looking into a crater, we'll see its structure. We'll learn about the bearing strength of the ground by pounding our feet. We'll learn an enormous amount just by crumbling the dust between our fingers. Will it crumble like powder, or will it stay hard like sand? That's the kind of thing we want to find out." Of the two astronauts, Lind is the more sanguine, Schmitt the more reserved. Both are civilians, and it is for this reason that they are unlikely to take part in the first landing. NASA feels that astronauts who have been military pilots may make slightly better spacecraft pilots—an important consideration on the initial mission. About two-thirds of the astronauts are military men, and of the remainder most are scientists, like Lind and Schmitt. The first men who have a chance of landing on the moon are two astronauts who will be on the Apollo 11 mission this summer—Colonel Edwin E. Aldrin, Jr., of the Air Force, and Neil A. Armstrong, who, though he is a civilian, might just as well be in the Air Force. Until recently, he was a professional test pilot who tested F-100's, F-101's, F-102's, and F-104's, and Air Force jet fighters; he has also flown the X-15—a small, mosquito-like airplane with a rocket inside it—at four thousand miles an hour, which is a good deal faster than the LM will be going when it approaches the moon. Though Lind and Schmitt have both taken flight training as astronauts, they are not professional fliers; rather, their special usefulness will be in making scientific observations when they get to the moon, possibly on Apollo 12, 13, or 14. Unlike Colonel Aldrin, who says that "the twists and turns of fate" have brought him his present assignment to land on the moon, Lind and Schmitt will arrive there as a result of conscious choice. Both have wanted to go there for some time. Lind, a trim, broad-shouldered man of thirty-nine, is a native of Murray, Utah; he served as a jet pilot in the Navy, and after his discharge, he got a Ph.D. in nuclear physics from the University of California. He says he became an astronaut because he saw space exploration as a way of combining physics and flying. (Becoming an astronaut isn't easy. A couple of years ago, when NASA made eleven new appointments to the astronaut corps, there were fifteen hundred applications.) Few astronauts offer romantic reasons for wanting to go to the moon, though one remarked once, "I wouldn't be happy unless I could live on the ragged edges of life." Lind and most of the other astronauts are notably sober-minded; in most cases, becoming an astronaut was a logical development of their earlier careers. After Lind received his Ph.D., he worked as a physicist at the Goddard Space Flight Center, in Greenbelt, Maryland, where he analyzed data sent back from the Orbiting Geophysical Observatory, a satellite that, among other things, radioed information about the fields of low-energy particles far above the earth. "I applied to be an astronaut because I thought science in space was important, and I guess I thought it would be easier if I were out there myself," Lind says. Schmitt's career wasn't much different. He is thirty-four years old, and is shorter and wirier than Lind. He was born in Santa Rita, New Mexico; graduated from the California Institute of Technology in 1957; and received a Ph.D. in geology from Harvard in 1964. Like Lind, Schmitt did work related to space before he became an astronaut. He was with the Astrogeology Branch of the United States Geological Survey, in Flagstaff, Arizona, where much of the geological analysis of the photographs of the lunar landscapes sent back by Surveyor and Orbiter spacecraft has been done. Having seen so many photographs of lunar rocks, he says, he wants to get his hands on the real thing.

Getting their hands on some lunar rocks will be the first thing the astronauts will have to do—or that the first astronaut to step onto the moon will have to do, for the other one will still be inside the LM. Not long ago, Dr. Urey said, "What I want the astronauts to do most of all is to fill their pockets brimful with pebbles, rocks, and dust—anything they can pick up." Dr. Urey would like it if there were some fossils in their pockets when they get back, but he will settle for anything. NASA regards bringing back some chunks of the moon as so vital that the first astronaut's first assignment is to pick up what NASA calls the contingency sample, but what the astronauts call the grab sample, possibly because they don't like to think in terms of contingencies. The "contingency" that NASA has in mind is any malfunction of the LM or of the astronauts' space suits, or any condition on the moon itself, that might necessitate a hasty retreat. NASA is providing a special tool for the two or three pounds of rubble that the sample will consist of.

Devising the best tools to use on the moon has taken a tremendous amount of effort, particularly among the human-factors engineers, who have to make sure that the man and the machine constitute a smoothly working unit, with the man completing the "control loop." One human-factors man recently defined a human being as "that erratic element of a system that is given to making unpredictable errors." The moon tools have to be virtually foolproof, since the astronaut may not be in the most levelheaded state when he comes to use them. The main requirement for the sample-grabbing tool is that it be simple enough for the astronaut to use effectively in a hurry. As reducing something to its simplest terms has never been one of NASA's strong points, the tool has gone through a long and complex evolution. Initially, there were two conflicting theories about the tool. One school of thought among human-factors engineers held that the astronaut should land on the moon, put down some sort of can (it would be of aluminum, the way most Apollo hardware is), and then scuff dirt into it with his feet. Another school of thought, which for a long time was in the ascendency, held that the tool should be a sort of scoop with a long, detachable handle. Lind, who has completed the control loop on a variety of cans and scoops that the human-factors engineers have wished to try out, was for a long time an advocate of the scoop with the detachable handle; one feature he liked about it was that the handle could be thrown away to save weight on the return trip. The tool that the astronauts will actually use on the moon—and that Lind now likes best—is similar to the latter one, only instead of being a scoop with a detachable handle, it is a sort of butterfly net with a detachable Teflon bag instead of a net. The hoop the bag is fastened to is about six inches in diameter and the handle is about twenty-five inches long; both are made of aluminum. In order to save space on the LM, the handle is collapsible, being made of several sections that are strung along a loose cable; accordingly, the astronaut's first job is to straighten out the handle, which he does by pulling on the cable, which ends in a grip that looks like a T. When the cable is tight, and the handle is straight, the astronaut slips the T into a slot. Lind says, "The astronaut could hang onto the LM's ladder with one hand, scoop up some dirt, and toss the sample up into the LM. If he is in a big hurry, he needn't even set foot on the moon himself." The astronaut won't *dig* into the moon, for the tool is too flimsy to use as a shovel; rather, he will scrape it around a few times. When the Teflon bag, which looks like an amber grocery bag, is full of grab sample—bulging, presumably, with blackish grit and perhaps an occasional pebble—the astronaut will remove it from the hoop, throw away the hoop and handle, crimp the bag shut with some aluminum strips, and stow it away inside the LM. For this kind of sample collection, the United States doesn't have to send a man all the way to the moon with a scoop; the same job could be done by an unmanned spacecraft, brandishing a scoop at the end of a mechanical arm, that could land on the moon and return to earth with the sample. It is entirely possible that the Russians will use this method. It could be cheaper than sending men, though NASA doesn't think it necessarily would be, given the cost of building an unmanned spacecraft sophisticated enough to do this kind of sample-gathering that NASA wants done. NASA scientists often cite one of the Surveyors, which landed beautifully on the moon, only to have the most interesting-looking rock just out of reach of its claws, which were made to snatch uselessly at it for several minutes. Frustrating as this experience was, however, it isn't NASA's main argument for sending men. As one geologist at the M.S.C. said recently, "There is a great temptation to see what a man can *do*." It is this that keeps the astronauts from being mere automatons, as they might be if the human-factors engineers succeeded in turning them into electronic components to complete the control loops of machinery. It also accounts for the great influence that the astronauts—and Lind and Schmitt in particular—have on plans for what they will do on the moon and the equipment they will have with them. Even Dr. Urey agrees that advancing science must take second place to testing the performance of the astronauts, at least on the first few trips. Schmitt says, "Finding out that we are *able* to fill the contingency-sample tool is just as important as bringing back the contingency sample itself. Once we know that, we can go on to more complex jobs. But first we have to know the answers to a number of questions. Can we act in one-sixth gravity? Is the visibility the way we thought? Can we see in the shadows?"

The astronaut's first job after landing and collecting the grab sample will be to see just exactly what he *can* do. He will walk about a bit, jump up and down a bit, and, to see how well his space suit works, perhaps bounce the way a man does in trying on a new pair of shoes—a series of movements that NASA calls "mobility evaluation." Science-fiction writers have always been fond of man's first few moments on the moon. In "The First Men in the Moon," which is the most literate though one of the least scientific books ever written about the moon, Wells' two astronauts, Mr. Cavor and Mr. Bedford, have trouble adjusting to the freedom of motion that accompanies low gravity, just as the Apollo astronauts will. Bedford, the narrator, takes a tumble, the result of overexuberance:

> I became aware of Cavor's little round face peering [down at me].... "We've got to be careful," he said. "This moon has no discipline. She'll let us smash ourselves."
>
> He helped me to my feet. "You exerted yourself too much," he said . . . "We don't quite allow for the gravitation. Our muscles are scarcely educated yet. We must practice a little. When you have got your breath."
>
> I pulled two or three little thorns out of my hand, and sat for a time on a boulder of rock. My muscles were quivering, and I had that feeling of personal disillusionment that comes to the learner of cycling on earth at his first fall.

Minus the thorns, this account may be a fairly accurate description of how the first and second astronauts will feel during their first moments on the moon.

In all likelihood, however, the Apollo astronauts won't have as giddy a time of it as Wells' pair, because NASA is a very safety-conscious outfit. The astronauts will be under strict orders not to try any long-distance jumping while they are evaluating their mobility. Just *walking* in the one-sixth gravity of the moon will be hard enough. Lind says the astronauts will constantly have the uneasy feeling that they are on the verge of floating off the moon altogether and disappearing into the big black yonder like wayward balloons. Although they will be only one-sixth their normal weight, their momentum will be the same as on earth, and this means that they will have trouble stopping once they get going, a difficulty that will be compounded because the astronauts, weighing less than they do here, will have less traction with the ground so they will be more apt to skid. Consequently, they may find themselves banging into things, for when an astronaut makes a turn, there will be an overpowering tendency for his body to keep going straight ahead, and less traction to prevent himself from doing so. Schmitt feels that the astronauts should study the way cats walk. "They are good at conserving angular momentum," he says. "A running cat can turn on a dime." What with the buoyancy and their sluggish steering, the astronauts may feel like badly ballasted ships lurching in a gentle swell; they may even feel a little seasick—a possibility that is mentioned by a veteran spaceman in Clarke's "Earthlight." This man comments solicitously to a friend who happens to be looking a bit green during his first lunar mission, "I was just wondering how you felt now. There's nothing worse than being sick in a space suit." The Apollo 8 astronauts, who were sick on the way to the moon, agree with this sentiment. One of them, Captain James A. Lovell, said afterward that he felt that in his case, at least, the trouble came from moving about fast too soon. He said that what happens "can be very similar to that queasy feeling you get if you are not used to being aboard ship—seasickness, to be exactly correct." Although the situation in the moon's one-sixth gravity may not be as severe as it is in space, the astronauts nonetheless will take it easy to avoid being seasick—or *spacesick,* to be exactly correct. (Properly speaking, astronauts have become seasick only after splashdown, while bobbing about in the ocean awaiting recovery.) Another matter that will make the astronauts move cautiously, at least until they get the hang of things, is the fact that on the moon, where there is no atmosphere to diffuse light, they may not be able to see into shadows. Involuntarily, they may give a wide berth to even small, shallow craters, because of shadows so inky that the craters will seem like bottomless pits. And, because the astronauts may find themselves tripping over rocks invisible in their own shadows, Schmitt says, one of the first tricks an astronaut may have to master is how to use his white suit to reflect light into shade, the way a surgeon used a metal reflector attached to his head. A tumble on a rock might damage a space suit. Recently a nervous space-suit designer explained, "The suit is tough enough so that the astronauts needn't pussyfoot around, exactly. However, there's no point in taking chances." The designer and his colleagues have taken none. For example, the backpacks, which contain the astronauts' life-support systems, are rounded. Initially, the pack was to have been square, but the square pack was discarded because the designers found that wearing it an astronaut who fell and landed on his back would have trouble rolling over in order to get up again. With the rounded pack, he will have no trouble rolling over; the only danger now would be if the pack became wedged into a crevice, a contingency that the designers have considered but don't think likely to happen.

As the astronaut wanders about the moon, he will look like a strange, apocalyptic knight who has strayed there from a crusade. His space suit is a milky white, to reflect the sunlight, but his helmet is a clear sphere, like a fishbowl, though it might appear gold if the visors are down. There are two visors, the inner one being clear like the helmet, but the outer one is golden, like some sunglasses, for a gold tint helps to filter out infrared and ultraviolet light, which could damage the astronaut's eyes. (Because there is no atmosphere, a greater range of sunlight reaches the moon than the earth.) Unlike sunglasses, the gold tint —real gold is used in coloring the visor—will not discolor the astronaut's view of the moon. The helmet is made of a clear, unbreakable, heat-resistant plastic called Lexan, which, in spite of its exceptional toughness, the astronauts will have to be careful of, for it scratches easily; the clear inner visor is to help protect it. Like the helmet for a suit of armor, the astronaut's helmet doesn't swivel, though the astronaut inside can turn his head wherever he wants. Outside, the space suit is a conglomeration of plugs for electric wires, attachments for hoses, and gauges that measure pressure and the like. There are pockets in unlikely places, such as at the ankles and shoulders, for such unlikely things as scissors, penlights, and checklists. The white outer layer of the space suit, which is made of a strongly heat-resistant glass fabric coated with a tough plastic, has a smooth, silky texture, like a good necktie. The astronauts will wear thick gauntlets and much thicker boots, which they call "lunar overshoes." The space suit and the portable life-support system are the most complex equipment the astronauts will have on the moon, except for the spacecraft itself. Occasionally, human-factors engineers get carried away and refer to the suit *as* a spaceship, calling it the fourth Apollo module—its predecessors being the command module, the service module, and the lunar module. And it is true that astronauts go out into space in nothing but space suits; all that the space suits lack to justify the engineers' claim is a rocket, and someday they may even have that. Like a spaceship, the suit is intended to protect the astronauts from radiation, extreme temperatures, and especially, the lack of pressure. The space suit is virtually an extension of the man inside it, following his movements, augmenting his lungs, and completing his metabolic cycle. The man is so thoroughly integrated into the suit, one human-factors engineer says, and the suit is so nearly a part of the man, that it is almost impossible to tell where one begins and the other leaves off. To human-factors men, this is the ideal relationship between a man and his equipment. (Schmitt says he wishes he and his suit were even better integrated, for his chafes him a bit.) Tailoring space suits isn't easy. For one thing, they have twenty-eight layers, or suits within suits. The outer layers are a shield against high temperatures outside. They also help protect the wearer against micrometeorites—particles of the diameter of a pin that are thought to shoot through space at speeds up to thirty miles a second and that could conceivably whoosh right through a man without his feeling anything more, possibly, than the sensation of a bee sting. (Fortunately, micrometeorites are not as prevalent as they were once thought to be.) The innermost layers are the heat-control layers, which double as the astronaut's underwear, and which keep the astronaut cool by means of a network of small pipes called Tygon tubing. These pipes circulate water through the suit and then through the backpack, where the heat is exhausted to the outside, in much the same way that a car radiator works. Between the outer shielding layers and the inner heat-control layers are the pressure layers, the rubbery part of the suit that is inflated with oxygen and that is perhaps the most indispensable part of the suit, for without it a man on the moon would be dead within a couple of minutes. This is because under extremely low pressure the fluids in the body start to boil. At the M.S.C., where there is a huge centrifuge capable of whirling men at speeds great enough to simulate low pressure, one man whose oxygen hose broke off his helmet while he was under conditions similar to those on the moon said later that before he passed out he could feel the saliva on his tongue bubbling away.

Lind says that the hardest part of the suit to get used to is the pressure. When his suit is inflated, Lind feels less like a white knight than like the rotund rubber man in advertisements for Michelin tires. Because of the pressure, the astronauts may find that they are easily fatigued, even though getting around in low gravity is theoretically all but effortless. Every time the astronaut moves, he has to push against the pressure—a difficulty that on earth only the Michelin-tire man may be familiar with. The arms and legs of the suit are pressurized cylinders, and they have to be broken whenever the astronaut bends an elbow or a knee. This breaking reduces and shifts the volume inside the suit, which then has to be made to expand somewhere else. The current solution to the problem is a sort of bellows arrangement at the elbows, the knees, and the other joints, so that when the elbow is bent, one side of the cylinder collapses and the other side expands. This makes movement easier than it would be otherwise, but it still isn't very easy. "Walking will be like shoving a crate across the moon," Schmitt says.

The stay on the moon will be strenuous for reasons other than the difficulty of moving about in space suits. "We'll be as busy as one-armed paperhangers," says Lind. Soon after gathering the contingency sample, the first astronaut on the ground will have inspected the LM for damage and begun to take dozens of photographs of the landing site and the LM with a special Hasselblad camera. Next, he will extract from a compartment in the LM a big, umbrella-like television antenna and set it up some thirty feet away, the second astronaut meanwhile joining him on the ground. (The second astronaut will have stayed inside the LM long enough to flick a switch to start TV transmission to earth.) By the time the second astronaut has slithered down the ladder to join the first, forty-five minutes may have elapsed. (One astronaut may go back into the LM from time to time, though presumably, if all is going well, they will both want to remain on the *mare*.) When the astronauts feel that they have their space suits, and the problems of moving around on the moon, more or less under control, they will begin gathering what is called the preliminary sample—a more thorough collection of dust, soil, and rocks than the contingency sample. Presumably, by this time most of the contingencies will have been successfully negotiated anyway. For the preliminary sample, the astronauts will have to go to a compartment at the back of the LM and pick up one of two boxes that NASA calls sample-return containers but that the astronauts call rock boxes. On later landings, the other rock box will be used later during the field trip, assuming that the astronauts stay on the moon long enough to make the geological expedition. (Along with the rock boxes, the compartment contains an assortment of geological tools including a hammer, a scoop, and a pair of tongs; a television camera with an assortment of lenses; some extra batteries for the life-support system in the backpack; a cartridge to restore the astronauts' oxygen supply; and a folding table that appears to be made of canvas but in fact is made of a fireproof material called Aclar. The astronauts will probably set the table up right away, so that they will have someplace besides the ground to put their equipment.) The rock box, nineteen inches long, ten and a half inches wide, and seven and a half inches high, is made of aluminum, but instead of being put together from several sheets, as cardboard boxes are, it is chemically hollowed out of an aluminum block, in order to make it leak-proof, for the samples in it must be kept in the same vacuum in which they were packed on the moon. (Hollowing the box out of a solid block also has the advantage of making the box lighter, since welding would add weight to it; the engineers are controlling the weight of the spaceship and its contents so closely that even the weight of a little solder is important to them.) The astronauts will carry the rock box at least a hundred feet from the LM, and they will toss into it as many different kinds of material as they can find, dumping them in without any attempt to sort the material, label it, or make a record of where it came from. That more detailed type of gathering comes later, when another pair of astronauts goes on the field trip. In the preliminary sample-grabbing, the astronauts will use the scoop, which has been designed so that the astronauts can fill the rock box with a very few scoopsful of dust and rock if they are in a hurry. The scoop is big and business-like, and it resembles a square-jawed steam-shovel scoop. Before he can use the scoop, the astronaut first has to attach it to a long extension handle, because he isn't able to reach closer than twenty-two inches from the ground, and he is forbidden to kneel or sit on the moon because the ground may be too hot, and, besides, he might also puncture the suit—or, as NASA prefers to say, "violate" the suit—on a sharp rock. He also would have a hard time getting up again. A man in a space suit is hardly agile. He can't bend at the waist, for the bellows arrangements in the space suit, which work well enough for the smaller joints like the elbows and knees, won't do for the larger ones, like the waist, where they tend to become unstable and balloon out dangerously. Similarly, the astronauts won't be able to reach above eye level, for the big bellows joints at the shoulders have to be held in by cables. Schmitt says the astronauts will be so restricted that every move they make, even a simple one like picking up a stone with the tongs, will have to be thought out in advance.

The astronauts have to carry the rock box a hundred feet from the LM in order to avoid contamination. Both the LM and the astronauts themselves will be a serious source of pollution to the moon—not so much with regard to the health of any selenites (though if there are any selenites, they had better watch out) as with regard to the integrity of the samples to be brought back to earth. The problem of contamination is taken very seriously, beginning at the Grumman Aircraft Engineering Corporation, where technicians in white uniforms are constantly looking through microscopes to check up on the dirt content of the clean room where the LM's are made. By the door to the clean room, whose atmosphere has to be filtered against particles one hundred and fifty times as small as the smallest that the eye can see, a card advertises a class in anti-contamination with the come-on "Get away from it all!" and presumably what one would be getting away from is the dirt described in a pamphlet pressed on all comers: "YOU—*People* are the greatest potential source of contamination in aerospace production facilities. Our bodies are continuously throwing off skin particles and broken hairs—millions of them in just minutes! Our every movement during work *increases* this rate of discard. The clean room is no place for horse-play, personal grooming, or even mild exercising—this could release as many as 30,000,000 *measurable* particles." Moving cautiously—perhaps even self-consciously—people entering the clean room put on enveloping smocks and blue surgical hats and then stand patiently in an electric shoe-polishing machine that does away with any lint on their feet. While they are waiting, they can look over another decontamination pamphlet featuring the gremlem, the space-age grandchild of the elflike gremlin who tampered with airplanes during the Second World War; the gremlem spends his time figuring ways to contaminate LM's. According to the pamphlet, one way to thwart gremlems is to wear plastic gloves—which quickly become unpleasantly hot and gummy—in order to avoid sending a fingerprint to the moon. Even so, the moon will probably not be unbesmirched. For example, one of the preliminary samples that the astronauts will collect is of the moon's exceedingly sparse atmosphere, a bit of which they will gather simply by opening a container, holding it up for a couple of seconds, and then sealing it shut, in the hope that a few molecules of lunar atmosphere will be trapped inside. They may well get more than they want. They may catch fumes from the LM's cabin, for before stepping outside the LM they will have had to depressurize it by exhausting the gasses inside to the outside, and even though these gasses (mainly oxygen) will have passed through a complex series of filters, they will still contaminate the moon in the vicinity of the LM. Far more serious is the fact that during the LM's landing its descent rocket will have discharged five tons of fumes into the moon's atmosphere. Because the weight of the moon's atmosphere is estimated at only a hundred tons (the earth's weighs between five and six quadrillion tons), the first lunar landing will pollute it to the extent of increasing it by five per cent. Undoubtedly, most of the lunar atmosphere that the astronauts catch in their jar will be rocket fumes. The descent rockets may also contribute to contamination in a far more subtle and confusing fashion, however, for the sample that the astronauts will have to gather with the greatest care is one for a group of scientists called exobiologists, who will be looking for traces of life on the moon. Exobiology, the study of extraterrestrial life, is such a new science that, as one exobiologist recently put it, apologetically, it is the only science that is, as yet, without any subject matter. When there *is* some subject matter, the exobiologists want to make sure that it is the real thing, and not a transplant from earth. This could be difficult to determine, because fumes might form organic compounds which could confuse the search for organic materials there. The exobiologists are worried about the astronauts, too, whose ability to pollute the moon one might assume to be severly curtailed by their being inside twenty-eight layers of space suit. At the space center, a geologist said, "Space-suit leakage doesn't bother us geologists very much, but it makes the exobiologists go straight up and turn left." (This is a fairly common expression among men at the space center.) From their perch at the upper left, the exobiologists have insisted that they will not come down again until the astronauts' cells—as well as bacteria—and other organisms which exobiologists call the astronauts' microflora have all been typed and catalogued for comparison later, lest a stray one be erroneously identified as a lunar organism.

In order to avoid capturing one of their own microflora

or gathering any of the other man-made contaminants on the surface of the moon, the astronauts will have to take the sample for the exobiologists from underground, and it must never be exposed to the surface of the moon or to anything else. They may wait until the second landing to gather it, though it is still scheduled for the first. To gather it, the astronauts will attach a small square box to the end of a long extension handle. The purpose of the box, which is open at the bottom, is to shield its contents from any of the astronaut's more venturesome microflora. First he puts the box on the ground and then he pushes down on the handle. Taking the aseptic sample is a little like taking a blood sample, for as he begins to push down, two metal scrapers inside the box push the topmost soil outwards, much as a doctor might swab a patient's skin before injecting a needle. As the astronaut continues to push down, a square tube sinks into the ground, filling up with whatever the moon is made of. When the tube is full, the astronaut pulls up on the handle, and as he does so, doors close across the bottom of the tube, sealing the sample inside. Then the astronaut shucks the box from the tube, which he discards like a doctor might throw away the protective part of a syringe; removes the extension handle; and finally tosses the tube into the rock box.

The possibility that there is life on the moon has tantalized men at least since the second century, when Lucian populated it with various mythological creatures in his "True History." More recently, in "The First Men in the Moon," Mr. Cavor, who was an eccentric scientist, saw "over the enormous disorder of rocks that formed the crater floor . . . the bristling scrub that . . . was starting into life, diversified here and there by bulging masses of cactus form, and scarlet and purple lichens that grew so fast they seemed to crawl over the rocks." NASA exobiologists don't expect anything as lush as this. In fact, the chances that there will be any form of life on the surface of the moon are very slim. There is not known to be any water on the moon, and there is an entirely inadequate atmosphere, a four-hundred-and-eighty-degree range in temperature, and ultraviolet light from the sun in quantities sufficient to kill any unprotected terrestrial organism. The surface of the moon would make a superb sterilizer for a hospital, for the best way to kill microscopic life is to put it in a vacuum, boil it, and expose it to ultraviolet light. However, this antiseptic environment alters considerably when just a few inches underground. Not only may a few inches of lunar soil be a sufficient blanket against the temperatures and the ultraviolet light, but many scientists, among them Dr. Urey, think that there may be water underground, and, given water, the chances for life just under the surface go up strongly. The type of life that the exobiologists will be looking for will not be anything like as complex as Wells' bristling scrub and cactus. The most they are hoping for is some form of microörganism, probably no more than just one cell. On earth, many of the different characteristics necessary for survival a few inches below the surface of the moon are to be found in a number of different microörganisms. (No single organism on earth has *all* the characteristics.) Like some fungi, a lunar microörganism would have to be capable of getting along without light. Like an anaerobe, it would have to be able to do without air. Though no known organism combines these two characteristics, there is no reason that one mightn't on the moon. If life exists anywhere in the subsoil of the moon, it may be that it will exist in the subsoil *everywhere,* or at least wherever there is water, for if lunar microörganisms are anything like earthly ones, they are adaptable and prolific. A sample of dirt taken from anywhere on earth, from the South Pole to the Sahara, will be crawling with microscopic forms of life. Therefore, if there is some underground life on the moon, the chances that the astronauts will catch some of it in the aseptic sample are not bad.

On the first trip to the moon, the astronauts will come home after they have collected their samples and, possibly, have laid out a few scientific instruments. (The astronauts making later trips will stay longer.) The man who will open the core sample when they get back may be Dr. Walter Kemmerer, a black-haired young scientist who got a medical degree from Baylor University in 1959 and is now chief of the Biomedical Specialties Branch at the M.S.C. Dr. Kemmerer says "aseptic sample" is a misnomer, for he hopes that the sample will be teeming with mysterious forms of microscopic life. He hasn't the slightest reason to think either that it might be or that it might not be, even though he is probably the leading expert on the chances of finding life on the moon. His office is a bare-looking room in the Lunar Receiving Laboratory, which is at present the most exciting place to be at the M.S.C., since the basic assumption upon which it was built was not just that the astronauts are *going* to the moon but that they have come *back.* The L.R.L. is the building to which the astronauts, the spaceship, and the samples will be brought when the trip is over.

Not unnaturally, Dr. Kemmerer is unwilling to commit himself on the possibility that life exists on the moon, though quite clearly his job and the L.R.L. itself are predicated on the possibility that it does. Dr. Kemmerer hedges neatly, in words bristling with double negatives: "We cannot definitely say that life does *not* exist on the moon, and in consequence we must take precautions to insure that we would not subject life on earth to any deleterious effects from lunar material." The chance that this will happen is extraordinarily remote. However, once scientists admit the possibility that there are microörganisms beneath the moon's surface, they must consider the possibility that on earth some of these might cause diseases of epidemic proportions, because life on earth would have built up no immunity to them. As Dr. Kemmerer talks about this ultimate "contingency," he has the slightly embarrassed air of a Texan who fears for his health when he enters a French restaurant but at the same time doesn't want to be called a hypochondriac. To cloak this sort of embarrassment, exobiologists have invented a nice-sounding clinical term to cover the contingency that we will all wake up dead shortly after the astronauts splash down in the Pacific. The term is "back-contamination," and mention of it will make any exobiologist go straight up and turn left in order to escape having to talk about it. The chances that back-contamination will occur are at once exceedingly remote and dreadful to contemplate. Like much else that NASA has been concerned with, the question of whether we will all be back-contaminated out of existence by lunar germs was handed over to a committee—the Inter-Agency Committee, made up of subcommittees from the Department of Agriculture, the Department of Interior, the Public Health Service, the National Academy of Science, and NASA itself. The committee recommended the expenditure of ten million dollars on the L.R.L., where the spacecraft, the astronauts, and the samples will be examined and quarantined until Dr. Kemmerer and the Inter-Agency Committee give them a clean bill of health. Dr. Kemmerer, who appears to feel a constant need to justify the expenditure on the lab, although he himself regards it as an obvious precaution, explains, a little defensively, that the way the Inter-Agency Committee arrived at the sum of ten million to be spent to guard against global catastrophe was by the use of a process similar to a formula that insurance companies use in computing premiums for fire or accident policies. The formula, which could be used to compile a sort of actuarial table for the world, is $P\hat{e} \times V = SV$, in which $P\hat{e}$ is the chance that there will be pernicious organisms on the moon; V is the value of the property being insured, which in this case is what one NASA scientist has referred to casually as the entire biosphere; and SV stands for Summated Value, which is the amount of insurance to be paid—in this case, the amount of money to be spent on the L.R.L. Dr. Kemmerer went on, "$P\hat{e}$, or the chance that dangerous organisms exist on the moon, is an almost infinitely small figure, but it isn't *quite* infinitely small, for it exists, and therefore could be expressed numerically. So could V, the value of the biosphere, which would be an enormously large figure. What the Inter-Agency Committee did to arrive at its conclusion was to multiply a very large figure by a very small one." Dr. Kemmerer did not have the figure for the chances of germs on the moon with him, nor did he have the figure for the total value of the world, but he clearly regards their multiple, ten million dollars, as an insurance premium that should be paid. (Congress, never known for its devotion to the biosphere, subsequently reduced the amount of money spent on the L.R.L. to $8,100,000.)

In the L.R.L., after the astronauts have returned, Dr. Kemmerer will examine all the samples, starting with the aseptic one, for signs of life, and then he will expose some of the samples to a culture material, to see if something will grow. He will also expose the samples to a variety of plant and animal life, and to that end the L.R.L. is to be stocked, like Noah's Ark, with a number of different plants and animals. *Unlike* Noah's Ark, which had lions and tigers and possibly a giraffe sticking its head out of a hatch, Dr. Kemmerer's laboratory will be heavy on algae and other forms of microscopic life. Among Dr. Kemmerer's larger animals—which include quail, oysters, shrimp, and cockroaches—is a colony of mice whose forebears, for several generations, have been reared in a completely antiseptic environment (even the air they breathe has been sterilized), so that they will be extremely receptive to any lunar germs.

The most sensitive index to the existence of lunar germs will be the astronauts, who will have been exposed to the moon itself, and they will have a special place in Dr. Kemmerer's laboratory. The astronauts will be under quarantine for twenty-one days, during which they will be treated as pariahs. The very air they exhale will be sterilized before it is allowed to pass back into the atmosphere. In their quarantine quarters at the L.R.L., moreover, the air pressure will be kept at a lower level than that of the atmosphere outside, so that if there is a leak, air will flow inward, not outward. A dozen other people will be quarantined with them, including two or three doctors, a cook, and probably a public-relations man. For twenty-one days, the astronauts may look out of a huge picture window, tinted brown against the Texas sun, at a particularly bleak section of the biosphere—an asphalt parking lot, which may make them think they are still on the moon. Just outside the window is a row of cactus-like plants, reminiscent of Wells. (The astronauts' view may be impaired in the event that the window is boarded up as a precaution against any crackpots who may want to toss rocks through it, releasing lunar germs.) At a press conference recently, Dr. Kemmerer was questioned closely by a group of reporters about whether twenty-one days was a sufficient quarantine period. He explained that although not all infectious diseases were covered by the twenty-one-day period, all known diseases that caused epidemics were, and epidemics were what he was chiefly worried about. The conference went on:

QUESTION: How are you prepared to handle something completely new to you? Say you find something in the sample? What would you do then?

KEMMERER: Indeed, if—The [quarantine] period is a first-cut, first-evaluation period. If at this time we find replicating material that is not readily identifiable as terrestrial form—well, then we go into the second order of testing, which is now in its development, which would give us a better hack, a better indication of what we are dealing with. If, indeed, after these second-order tests are completed, still others are indicated, using larger animals, and other forms of research—well, then there are laboratories that could support the effort from around the country. . . .

QUESTION: Is this a concern you people have?

KEMMERER: We recognize certainly the extreme unlikely event, it would be difficult to place a number on it, but it is extremely unlikely. We don't think it precludes the necessity of our considering what our alternative would be should it occur.

QUESTION: What would be the procedure if . . . some type of organism was found in the sample either before the crew was released from the quarantine or after it?

KEMMERER: This depends upon what was found in the sample. Certainly . . . the crew had a very minimal exposure, they had been in a positive pressurized suit on the lunar surface. . . . So we feel this is a very minimal exposure, it's one that we must certainly take into consideration. . . .

The questions kept on coming.

PART II
Working

When the astronauts get back to the LM, they will be carrying approximately twenty-five pounds of rock and dust (weighing slightly over four pounds on the moon), including the core tube with Dr. Kemmerer's aseptic sample. They will seal the rock box, which looks like one of the vacuum boxes used on picnics to keep sandwiches and soft drinks cold; it will keep the lunar samples in a vacuum like the moon's until it is unpacked at the Lunar Receiving Laboratory. Using a rope-and-pulley system, which the first astronaut will have set up on his way down the ladder, they will hoist the rock box to the top of the descent stage of the LM. (The LM is in two parts; on top is the ascent stage, which is the spacecraft in which the astronauts will leave the moon, and below it is the descent stage, an octagonal platform, which will serve as a launching pad for their departure and will be left behind. The astronauts don't care what happens to the descent stage after they take off, though they want it to stay together until they are away. The ascent engine, which looks like a bell though it is invisible now to the astronauts, has only thirty-five hundred pounds of thrust as compared with ten thousand pounds for the engine that landed the astronauts on the moon—an indication of how much weight the astronauts will leave behind them. Most of this, of course, will be the descent stage, and with the American flag painted on its side, it will be the closest the astronauts will come to planting the flag on the moon.) By hauling away on the rope from the ground, one of the astronauts will cause the box to bump eleven feet up the side of the LM's descent stage, until it disappears at last onto the platform. The astronauts want the box up there so that they can push it quickly through the hatch into the LM's cabin if they have to leave in a hurry. One reason the astronauts might have to leave in a hurry is that they might get word from Houston that a solar flare—a storm on the sun, which would drastically increase radiation on the moon—was boiling up; in that case, the astronauts would have to be inside the LM and off the moon in a matter of minutes. Assuming that all is quiet on the sun, and on the moon, too, the astronauts will go about their next chore, which is to set up something called the Early Apollo Scientific Experiments Package. (It is "early" only in that it is to be deployed before the more complex Apollo Lunar Surface Experiments Package, which may be set up, at least in part, during the second Apollo landing; because no one is certain how strenuous working on the moon will be, the doctors at the M.S.C. want to see how the astronauts do with the simpler package first.) The Early Package consists of three relatively simple scientific instruments: a seismometer; a mirror, which astronomers on earth will bounce a laser beam from in order to measure the distance of the moon from the earth, which a laser can do with an accuracy of a few feet; and a large sheet of aluminum foil, which the astronauts will unfold on the *mare* and later fold up again and bring back to earth—teeming, presumably, with particles of the solar wind, a stream of atoms and particles that is always radiating away from the sun. Finally, if there is still time, one or both astronauts may go for a short walk (no more than a few hundred feet) to pick up more samples. After that, they will head home.

The later trips will be much like the first, except that more time will be spent setting up scientific instruments, and still more time than that will be devoted to the geological field trip, during a second three-hour excursion outside the LM. The second lunar landing, probably Apollo 12, may come next October. During this landing and subsequent ones, the astronauts will start off much as they did on the first trip; that is to say, they will gather contingency and preliminary samples, because each landing will presumably be made at a different place, and the scientists will be anxious to compare samples from various parts of the moon. Then, in the hour or so remaining to them in their first period of extra-vehicular activity, or E.V.A., they will go on to deploy the ALSEP—the Apollo Lunar Surface Experiments Package.

Most of the ALSEP experiments are designed to look below the surface and into the interior of the moon. At a NASA conference held at Falmouth, Massachusetts, in the summer of 1965, where the type of scientific research that the astronauts would be asked to do was discussed, the scientists present agreed that since a fair amount would be known about the moon's surface from the Surveyor and Orbiter flights, the most constructive contribution that Apollo could make would be to study the moon's interior. One of the main reasons for doing this is that if the structure of the moon proves to be similar to the earth's—that is, to have a core, a mantle, and a crust—then geologists may be able to learn a good deal about the structure of the earth, for the moon is so much smaller than the earth that the geologists' instruments can peer a good deal farther inside. This type of study is often called comparative planetology, and, indeed, more and more astronomers are coming to look upon the moon less as a satellite than as a twin planet of the earth's, the earth and the moon constituting a dual planetary system rather like that of the double stars, though these revolve around each other. And the moon may once have *been* a planet, revolving independently around the sun. Certainly the moon is larger in relation to the earth than any other known moon is in relation to its planet. Since the moon may be a planet, the measurements to be made there are the same ones geologists and physicists have for years been making on the planet earth. NASA scientists think of the ALSEP as a complete, though very simple, unmanned scientific station of a type that the United States Geological Survey might operate here. The first ALSEP will include a so-called passive seismic experiment, to measure moonquakes; a magnetometer, to measure the moon's magnetic field, if any; a gauge to measure the electronic particles of the solar wind; and a machine to measure what is thought to be an ionosphere encircling the moon near the ground. Later ALSEP's will contain different experiments, including one to measure the flow of heat from the center of the moon. In each of the ALSEP's, there is, in addition to the measuring instruments, a central station to transmit the data from the experiments to Houston, and a small power generator with radioactive fuel, to keep the experiments working and the central station transmitting data for at least a year. Although the experiments are as simple and solid as they can be, deploying the ALSEP is the most intricate single chore that the astronauts will have to perform while they are on the moon, and the human-factors men have been having a field day with it.

At Ann Arbor, Michigan, where the Aerospace Systems Division of the Bendix Corporation has its headquarters, a human-factors engineer, working alone, set up the ALSEP in exactly forty-six minutes and three seconds. He says that on the moon it will take the two astronauts quite a bit longer than that. First, the astronauts will walk around to the rear of the LM, where the ALSEP is stowed in an outside compartment behind one of the eight panels that make up the octagonal descent stage. The panel, like that on the compartment the rock boxes were stored in, opens the way some garage doors do, the doors folding together in sections horizontally, then upward, and, finally, back into the top of the compartment. Inside are what look like two white drawers, one above the other, with a handle set into the front of each; the drawers are the two subpackages, as the engineers call them, that make up the ALSEP. Probably the astronauts will pull the two subpackages out by their handles and put them on the ground; however, if the LM is tilted, the handles may be out of reach of the astronauts, since they cannot raise their hands above their heads. In that event, one of the astronauts will take hold of one end of a rope inside the compartment. When he walks away from the compartment, the rope will raise a small, cranelike boom; next, as he keeps walking away, the subpackages are lifted out; and then, when he walks toward the LM again, they are lowered gently to the ground. The human-factors engineers are particularly proud of this arrangement. Together, the two cases weigh upward of two hundred pounds, or about thirty-four pounds on the moon. In Subpackage

No. 1 are three of the experiments and the central station; the fourth experiment is in Subpackage No. 2, along with the small generator.

The fuel for the ALSEP's generator is a radioactive isotope that, because its temperature is fourteen hundred degrees, has to make the trip to the moon in a small metal bottle attached to the outside of the LM. The bottle—or fuel cask, as it is called—is attached to the descent stage adjacent to the compartment the ALSEP is in, and is painted black and bronze like the LM itself. Because the fabric that the space suits are made of melts at a temperature considerably lower than the exterior temperature of the fuel cask, the astronauts have been quite concerned about the possibility of their inadvertently bumping into the cask, and Lind has been giving the human-factors engineers something of a hard time about this possibility. As a result, part of the door into the ALSEP compartment will open sideways, instead of upward, so that it will become a shield to one side of the cask. However, Lind pointed out that the astronauts could still bump into the cask from straight ahead or from the other side, so the human-factors engineers came up with a couple of struts, like the bars of a cage, to be put around the cask; they are made of a metal that will not get too hot. One gets the impression sometimes that the entire space industry hangs on every word the astronauts utter. "We get a lot of astronaut feedback, and we listen to what they have to say," one human-factors engineer said recently. (The computer seems to have had a strong impact upon the language spoken by space engineers.) "We find them very serious people. If you're not involved with them, you might think they were a little picky. But they're the ones that are going on this trip. So we listen to them. Every time Lind or any other astronaut opens his mouth, the entire space industry turns flip-flops."

The entire industry has been turning flip-flops trying to insure that the astronauts get the hot fuel out of the cask and into the ALSEP's generator without damaging their suits. Lind says that transferring the fuel is the most dangerous job the astronauts will have to do on the moon, short of taking off and landing. "The danger will be equivalent to that of a man who isn't used to carpentry working around an open buzz saw," he says. The job will be particularly dangerous on the moon because heat travels freely through a vacuum. One astronaut will do the job alone using two long-handled tools—one to remove a domelike lid on top of the cask, and the other to lift out the hot fuel—which is a task that Lind feels will be like feeding a lion with a teaspoon. Transferring the fuel is a complicated operation. At the Bendix Corporation, the human-factors engineer who did the time-and-motion study for laying out the ALSEP loaded the fuel into the generator and then produced a timetable—NASA calls it a "time line"—for the astronauts' benefit:

1. Remove Dome Removal Tool (DRT)	5 seconds
2. Walk to fuel cask	5 seconds
3. Mate DRT with dome-locking mechanism	10 seconds

4. Press inward on DRT and rotate dome-locking mechanism 90° counterclockwise	5 seconds
5. Pull outward on DRT and rotate dome 60° counterclockwise	10 seconds
6. Remove dome and discard DRT/dome	10 seconds
7. Return to Package No. 2 [where the generator is]	5 seconds
8. Remove Fuel Transfer Tool (FTT)	10 seconds
9. Rotate Package No. 2 to the fueling position	5 seconds
10. Walk to fuel cask	5 seconds
11. Insert FTT fingers into fuel capsule head	15 seconds
12. Engage FTT fingers in fuel capsule head by rotating knob clockwise	15 seconds
13. Withdraw fuel capsule from fuel cask	10 seconds
14. Turn to Package No. 2	5 seconds
15. Lower fuel capsule into Radioisotope Thermoelectric Generator (RTG)	5 seconds
16. Report RTG fueled [to Houston]	2 seconds
17. Disengage FTT fingers from fuel capsule head by counter-rotation of knob	10 seconds
18. Discard FTT	5 seconds

Despite this schedule, the astronauts have a pretty good idea of what they are doing, and so are not likely to be confused. Nevertheless, setting up the ALSEP is hardly likely to constitute one of the joys of being on the moon; the astronauts would much rather be exploring and making observations of their own, as they will be doing later, on the field trip. Lind once asked some engineers at Bendix whether they couldn't design the ALSEP so that all the astronauts had to do to deploy it was to press a button. The engineers said that they could, but would rather that the astronauts did more than that.

The astronauts, possibly in a ruffled frame of mind, will next carry the ALSEP, in its two subpackages, a hundred yards from the LM, where the experiments, after they are set up, will be out of range of the blast of the LM's takeoff rocket. The human-factors engineers, who have been no less idle in the matter of transporting the ALSEP than they were in the matter of transferring the fuel, have come up with a means of transportation they call the Barbell Carry Mode. The Barbell Carry Mode was settled on after every conceivable way of carrying two heavy packages had been looked into. The most obvious method—carrying the two packages by their handles, like suitcases—was discarded almost at once, because the packages are too clumsy for that. Other traditional methods—that is, *modes*—of carrying two objects that were considered and discarded were hauling them on a sledge and dragging them on a travois, a primitive arrangement used by Apache Indians and consisting of two poles trailing from the shoulders with a platform slung between them. (The travois was discarded because it might run afoul of the astronaut's backpack, among other reasons.) At length, it was decided to secure the two packages to either end of a sturdy pole, so that one astronaut could carry the ALSEP at waist level, like a barbell. (The pole later converts into a radio mast for communications between the ALSEP and earth.) The barbell method, in the opinion of the human-factors engineers, has many advantages. For one, Subpackage No. 1 is heavier than Subpackage No. 2, and the astronaut can balance the load easily by positioning his hands a little closer to the heavier end of the barbell. For another, the astronaut will be able to see his feet—a prime human-factors requirement for men on the moon, lest he stumble on a rock. According to the Bendix timetable, it will take nine minutes and forty-five seconds for the astronauts to walk the one hundred yards to the site.

These may be the most strenuous nine minutes and forty-five seconds of the entire stay on the moon, at least for the astronaut saddled with the barbell. Given the extra effort it takes to move around in a space suit anyway, the astronaut with the barbell may find himself beginning to perspire. Schmitt says that the inside of a space suit can get a little like a small gymnasium during a big game. A Gemini astronaut worked up such a lather while he was floating in space outside a capsule that his helmet fogged over, temporarily blinding him. This happened to a character in Clarke's "Earthlight," too; he found that after a half-hour hike on the moon his face plate had misted so badly that he had to peer out of the corners in order to see. As the astronaut progresses slowly across the dark-gray *mare,* balancing his load in front of him, he may hear a small voice in his ear suggesting that he slow down and take it easy for a while. This amiable advice will come from a doctor in the Mission Control Center at the M.S.C. who is monitoring the astronaut's heartbeat, there being a direct correlation between the astronaut's pulse and his metabolic rate—the rate at which he puts out heat. Inside his space suit, the astronaut has a number of sensors that report on the state of his health, in much the same way that the instruments in the ALSEP will report on the processes that go on inside the moon. Back at the M.S.C., a team of experts—made up of engineers who know about the life-support system, physiologists who know about the functioning of the body, and even ordinary physicians—will be monitoring such things as the astronaut's respiration and pulse; they will be reporting on his condition to the flight surgeon, who from time to time may tell the astronaut to slow down. The doctors' biggest concern is that the astronaut's ability to generate heat can at times exceed the ability of the water-filled Tygon capillaries threading the suit to take the heat away. Though the heartbeat is a fairly good index of metabolic rate and of the body's capacity to generate heat, it isn't infallible, for sometimes thoughts or emotions can send a man's pulse soaring. At one point during Colonel Aldrin's Gemini 12 flight, his pulse shot up dangerously and stayed up for two minutes, creating confusion and alarm among the doctors at the Mission Control Center; then they discovered that during those two minutes Aldrin, evidently a sentimental and patriotic soul, was reading a Veterans Day message to the ground.

The Apollo astronauts won't be reading any Veterans Day messages from the moon. Inside the two packages the astronaut is carrying, the ALSEP experiments, the generator, and the central station will be fitted together as tidily as the pans, cups, and knives in the cooking kit of a more earthly explorer, which the ALSEP somewhat resembles. When the astronaut has set the ALSEP down on a suitably craterless and rockless area—the kind of even terrain an explorer would pitch his tent on—they start to work unpacking the experiments. Almost all the equipment is a milky white, in order to reflect the sun's heat. First they unpack the radioisotope thermoelectric generators in Subpackage No. 2. This generator, which the astronauts, like everyone else who has to talk about it, call the R.T.G., is a cylindrical can with long metal fins radiating from it. When they have put down the R.T.G., which by now is almost as hot as the fuel inside it, the astronauts move the two subpackages ten feet farther on, so that they won't have to risk going near the R.T.G. again. The only item left in Subpackage No. 2 is the magnetometer, which looks very much like a folded campstool. Next, the astronauts start to work on Subpackage No. 1, which has a good deal more in it, and which looks like a Coleman stove with three oddly shaped pots on top of it. The Coleman stove is the central station, and the three pots are the passive seismic experiment, the solar-wind experiment, and the suprathermal-ion-detector. The top of the stove is a collapsible sunshield, which has been folded down for the trip. Because the experiments are bolted to it, the astronauts will have to remove them and set them up before they can get around to setting up the central station itself. To set up the central station, they will first have to put the sunshield in place. They will do this by lifting it up on four collapsible legs. As the shield lifts, the central station will turn into a sort of pup tent, for a curtain unfolds to fill the area between the sunshield and the central station. Finally, they will place the antenna on its mast, which they were using as a barbell, making sure that it is aimed at the blue earth high overhead.

The human-factors engineers turned some more flip-flops in figuring out how to unfasten the experiments, carry them to their appointed place, and set them up. Every movement in deploying the ALSEP is made close to the ground, and since the astronauts can't bend over, this presents a problem. The human-factors engineers solved the problem by inventing a tool called the universal handling tool, which is perhaps the only strictly new tool designed for use on the moon, all the other equipment having some resemblance to objects used on earth. The tool, which is white, like the rest of the ALSEP, looks like a long, slender crank. It is L-shaped, with a shank twenty-six inches long and a handle, at right angles, six inches long. Although the tool is quite simple, it took the engineers two years to develop it, the tool taking first one form and then another, and each form being thought for a while to constitute the final version. Nearly all the Apollo equipment has undergone a similarly slow, careful evolution because nearly all of it, though it wasn't being invented from scratch, at least had to be adapted to specialized use on the moon—a circumstance that goes a long way to explain why the Apollo Project is so expensive.

The job of developing the universal handling tool was assigned to some engineers at the Bendix Corporation's Aerospace Systems Division, at Ann Arbor. One of them was Mr. Angelo J. Micocci, chief of the crew engineering group, who is a stocky, black-haired man in his early forties. Though a thorough, meticulous worker, the way all human-factors engineers are, Mr. Micocci is nonetheless staggered by the amount of work that went into the tool. The universal handling tool started out as two separate tools—one a sort of screwdriver, for unfastening the experiments, and the other a lifter, for picking up the experiments and carrying them. In planning the tool for unfastening the experiments, Mr. Micocci and his associates first had to look over designs for equipment on the market—equipment produced by over fifty companies. None of them would do. Bendix at last developed a sort of enlarged screwdriver, which went through several different phases of production and was almost "finalized," Mr. Micocci says, when NASA "gave it the buy-off"—that is, bought it but didn't use it. NASA felt it was harder for an astronaut to fit the tool onto the screws on the ALSEP than it ought to be. In a space suit, a man cannot twist his wrist very much, so it is difficult for him to place a screwdriver on a screw unless he is standing in exactly the right position. Back at the drawing board, Mr. Micocci and his colleagues came up with a nut-and-bolt arrangement that, because the nuts and bolts have twelve sides, can be unfastened from a great many more angles.

The bolts—they are called Boyd bolts, and there are to be a total of eighteen of them on the experiments—have to fasten the experiments down with five hundred pounds' pressure to withstand the jolt of the takeoff from Cape Kennedy, yet they have to be loosened with a minimum of turning to make things easier for the astronauts. At first, the bolts took just three-quarters of a turn to release, and Mr. Micocci and his colleagues thought that that would be acceptable to NASA. It wasn't. A man in a space suit can twist his wrist—or a wrench—only *one*-quarter of a turn before he has to shift his grip. At that rate, the astronaut on the moon would have to shift his grip twice in removing each Boyd bolt, and this would mean that he risked letting the tool slip through his thick-gloved hands on each of the shifts. If the tool should drop on the ground, it would be hard to pick it up again, for the astronauts have no tool designed to pick up a dropped universal handling tool. The unfastening system that Bendix finally came up with, and that NASA bought, can be undone with one-fifth of a turn.

While all this was going on, the tool for lifting and carrying the experiments was undergoing a similar metamorphosis. The carrying tool has something in common with an old-fashioned stove-lid handle, though it works in an entirely different way. The shank of the tool sticks into a hole on the top of the experiment to be carried, and then some metal balls on the shank slip neatly under the lip inside of the hole, so the astronaut can lift the experiment by the tool. The balls are locked in place or released—and the shank slips in and out of the hole in the experiment—when the astronaut pulls a trigger on the handle with his index finger. Even the design for the trigger took an enormous amount of fiddling. Until very recently, the designers wanted to use a button, which the astronaut would have pressed with his thumb. A trigger, which they had discarded earlier, would be hard for the astronaut to pull, because the palms of the space suit's hands have solid metal plates in them. This is to prevent the hands from ballooning out from the pressure inside the suit every time the astronaut moves his fingers, for the palms are unstable joints like the shoulders; the metal plates act like the battens that prevent sails from billowing. With the metal plate in the middle of the astronaut's palm, the designers felt that he would have a hard time moving his fingers or doing much in the way of pulling triggers, and hence the trigger was dropped in favor of the button, which the astronaut would press by a sort of rolling motion with his thumb. Because of the rolling motion, which meant that the button had to be offset from the handle, the button mechanism turned out to be too bulky to satisfy another group of engineers whose job it is to figure out how to pack all the equipment into the LM, and so when the space-suit designers came up with a better design that made the astronaut's hands more agile—they made the metal plate a different shape—the hand-tool engineers reverted to the trigger. They had actually preferred the trigger all along, because an astronaut can exert more pressure on it. The trigger pulls like a pistol's, moving about three-eighths of an inch.

The trigger wasn't the only part of the hand tools that was affected by changes in the design of the space suit. The shank of each of the tools, for instance, caused

Mr. Micocci as much trouble as any other part, for every time he thought the tools were more or less in final form, word would come from NASA that the shank had to be a little longer. This was because the designers of the space suit kept making the backpack bigger, and with each increase in the backpack the astronaut could lean over less and, consequently, would need longer tools to reach the ground. The tools, which started out being four inches long, grew first to eight inches, then to sixteen inches, then to twenty-two inches, and, finally, to twenty-six inches. Then, when the two separate tools really did seem to be more or less in their final form, NASA demanded that they be combined into one. "We came up with the universal handling tool," Mr. Micocci says, a little wearily. The most wearisome part of the whole project was the amount of paperwork involved, for every change involved numerous meetings between Bendix and NASA, an outfit that believes that safety lies in numbers of committee meetings. Mr. Micocci feels the effort was worth it, though, because, he says, "we don't want to leave anything to chance—we want to iron out all the wrinkles before the astronauts get to the moon."

Possibly unaware of the number of wrinkles that have been smoothed out of the universal handling tool, one of the astronauts will apply it to the Boyd bolts, and, after a number of brisk one-fifth turns, will be ready to begin setting up the experiments. He will have to brace himself better than he would on earth, his feet far apart and perhaps slightly dug into the gritty black *mare*, because, in the low gravity, untwisting the bolts would tend to spin the astronaut in the other direction—another reason he will be glad the bolts require only a fifth of a turn. Though the order in which the experiments are to be set up varies from one NASA meeting to another, the first one could be the passive seismic experiment, which will be recording moonquakes. It is fastened to the sunshield by four bolts. The astronauts will carry it, impaled on the universal handling tool, ten feet to the east of the central station, and will make sure that it is at least fifteen feet away from the R.T.G., because the heat of the radioactive fuel could interfere with the measurements that the experiment will be making. As the astronaut walks along, an electrical cord attaching the experiment to the central station will unreel behind him. He or the other astronaut will already have carried a small stool, which he will drop on the ground for the experiment to sit on. The stool is simply a metal ring on three legs. The experiment is a can fifteen inches high and eleven inches in diameter, its bottom rounded so that it fits onto the stand much as an ancient amphora would fit on its stand. The rounded bottom will make it easier for the astronaut to swivel the experiment into exactly the right position. There are four metal tabs at the base of the experiment, and he will push against these with the handling tool in order to get the experiment perfectly level. He can tell when the experiment is level by looking at a steel ball rolling around in a small dish set into the middle of its top. The ball in the dish is a more practical level on the moon than a carpenter's bubble in a glass, for in the low gravity an ordinary carpenter's level might blow up. Not only does the experiment have to be level but it has to be directed toward the east. Around the top of the experiment is a numbered dial, and the astronaut has to nudge the experiment so that the "O" on the dial is pointing toward the sun. Then he has to radio back to Houston the points on the dial where a shadow cast by a bump on top of the experiment (the bump made by the leveling gauge) falls, so that the scientists back at Houston can figure out *exactly* how the experiment is set. The dial is coated with a luminous orange paint called International Orange, a psychedelic color glaringly visible against the milky-white experiment. Though it is glaringly visible on earth, Mr. Micocci, to leave absolutely nothing to chance, had to make sure it would be equally visible on the moon. Accordingly, the experiment, dabbed with the orange paint, was put into a dark chamber simulating the moon—the walls were covered with a black honeycomb material to prevent any scattering of light, and the floor was covered with a moon-like mixture of dark-gray sand and gravel. Even so, the paint leaped out as eye-catchingly as it would from a Times Square billboard.

Next, the astronauts have to spread on the ground around the experiment a circular tarpaulin made of a shiny silver material called Mylar. Mylar is a tough, crinkly material, much like Reynolds Wrap, and it is used not only for the experiment but also as insulation in the spacecraft. (In approving materials for Apollo flights, NASA has to bear in mind so many factors, such as weight, combustibility, and toxicity, that any material that has once been approved, as Mylar has been, is likely to be used over and over again by contractors who want to avoid trouble. Another example is Teflon, which is used in the space suit, for durability, and also as material for the small bags that the astronauts who go on the field trip will put their geological samples into. Other materials that NASA approves of—all are synthesized for their special properties—include Tygon, the material used for the space suit's cooling system; Aclar, the material for the blinds inside the LM; and Kapton, the insulation inside the spacecraft. Tygon, Teflon, Mylar, Aclar, and Kapton all have a way of sounding as though they were the names of beings on a different planet.) The purpose of the Mylar tarpaulin, which is officially known as the thermal shroud, is to insulate the ground around the seismometer so that it won't expand or contract with the lunar heat or cold, shifting the experiment. The human-factors engineers had a tough time deciding exactly how the shroud should be folded around the experiment so that the astronauts could unfold it with the least possible trouble. First, the engineers pleated it around the can, but this didn't work; when a human-factors engineer in a space suit tried to unfold the shroud with the universal handling tool, the can kept falling off the trivet. Mr. Micocci explains, "The friction of the folded pleats was greater than the friction exerted by the passive seismic experiment against the stool." In order to reduce the friction of the folded pleats, the human-factors engineers decided to fold the shroud neatly around the experiment in such a way that before it is unfolded it will look like a budding tulip. On the trip, the folds will be held in place by a wrapping, which the astronauts will have to remove. Using the universal handling tool, the astronaut will flip (but will not pull) the folds one by one onto the ground, until the experiment is sitting in the center of a Mylar pentagon. The astronaut will have to unfold the pentagon until it makes a circle, and to do so he has to make sure that he gets hold of the correct fold first. Accordingly, that fold is marked in International Orange with the number 1 and an arrow pointing to a tab where he is to insert the universal handling tool. The second is marked with the number 2, but the other pleats will not be numbered, because, by the time the astronaut has unfolded the first two, he will be going in the proper direction. "We don't want to confuse him with more numbers than are necessary," says Mr. Micocci, who may be trying to make up for the complexities of the Bendix time-and-motion schedule. When the astronaut is done, the experiment will be sitting like an island in the middle of a brilliant silvery pool of Mylar spreading five feet across the black *mare.* It is so bright that the astronauts' ability to see in the dark may be temporarily impaired, so the human-factors engineers have to make sure that the next few chores the astronauts perform are in full sunlight. Actually, the astronauts are apt not to follow any schedules once they get to the moon, for they like to think they are running their own show. They appreciate the meticulous arrangements that the human-factors engineers are trying to make ahead of time, but they get irritated by them, too. Recently, one astronaut reminded a human-factors expert, "When I first set foot on the moon, *I* will be the leading expert on lunar human factors."

One lunar human factor that the astronauts are consulting human-factors engineers about here on earth is the possibility that, as they lay out more of the experiments, they will become increasingly apt to trip over the wires connecting the experiments to the central station. Before the astronauts are done, the ALSEP will look like a spiderweb, with trails of wire radiating in all directions. Lind says, "One of the things we fear most is getting tangled in a cord and taking a header on top of an experiment." The human-factors engineers have tried to arrange matters so that the astronauts need never walk over a cord once it is laid down. Also, the cords, which have up to thirty-two individual wires in them, will be ribbons that lie flat on the ground, making it harder to trip over them. The cords are easier to stow that way, too.

With the passive seismic experiment in place, the astronauts have three to go. The next experiment to be unbolted and set in place—with a trail of white ribbon unwinding behind it across the blackish *mare*—may be the solar-wind experiment, which is a rectangular box thirteen inches high, nine inches wide, and eleven inches long. It looks like a small carton with an explorer's pith helmet tossed on top of it. The astronauts will lug it fourteen feet south of the central station—away from the R.T.G., which could interfere with it—and then open up four collapsible legs it is to stand on. Setting up this experiment took a minute and thirty-four seconds when some human-factors engineers tried it at Bendix, but it will doubtless take longer than that on the moon. When the experiment is working, the solar wind will stream through some windows in the dome on its top and be recorded by sensors inside. By measuring this flow of electrons, protons, atoms, and charged particles from the sun, scientists hope to be able to tell such things as precisely the amount of atmosphere the moon has and whether the moon is a good conductor of electricity.

Next may come the magnetometer, which is a square box with three arms protruding upward from it, and which an astronaut will have to carry fifty feet from the central station, in the direction away from the LM. If it were set up closer, the blast when the LM takes off could jar the arms out of alignment. At the end of the three arms, each of which is about two feet long, there is a delicate sensor for measuring the moon's magnetic field. The sensors may also pick up the magnetic fields of the sun and the earth, for these fields flow through and about the moon. The astronauts will have to make sure that one of the arms points due east, toward the sun; the leg below that arm will be striped with International Orange and, lest the astronaut be forgetful, the top of the instrument will be emblazoned with an arrow and the letter "E," for east. (The astronaut has to remove the "E" and the arrow because International Orange, Mr. Micocci found, absorbs heat.) The arms wave in the air like the legs of a campstool upside down. The final experiment, the suprathermal-ion-detector experiment—its acronym is SIDE—is a rectangular box standing eight inches high and weighing twelve pounds. The astronauts carry it fifty-five feet from the central station, making sure that it is at least eighty feet from the magnetometer, because the part of SIDE which has a big magnet might interfere with it. (One of the principal difficulties of laying out the ALSEP is that each experiment has to be in a special position in relation to the others.) Indeed, SIDE is so delicate that the astronaut must first lay down a mat of wire mesh for it to stand on. This is to overcome any magnetic or electric field emanating from the moon, for the purpose of the experiment is to measure ions that are believed to compose a low-lying ionosphere just above the surface. The astronaut has to align a slit at the top of the instrument with the ecliptic—the path of the sun. While the astronauts are setting up SIDE, they will also set up a sort of satellite of SIDE, a tiny experiment the size of a kitchen matchbox, called the cold-cathode-gauge experiment, which will measure the density of the lunar atmosphere. This instrument, which has no acronym, but which the astronauts sometimes call the sidekick, will be put down about four feet from SIDE, to which it is connected by a round cable. This experiment is the most temperamental of all, in that the astronaut cannot face it toward anything else—not toward SIDE, or toward any of the other experiments, or toward the LM, or even toward the earth or the sun.

Almost any experiment can be designed to plug into the central station, so different Apollo flights to the moon will involve different ALSEP's. On the third or fourth flight, the ALSEP will include an instrument for measuring the heat that escapes from the surface of the moon. To put this in place an astronaut will have to drill two holes ten feet deep into the black soil of the *mare*. Then he will drop a three-foot heat probe—a sort of thermometer—down each hole. The moon is small enough so that if it has a hot, liquid core radiating heat, there should be a slight difference in the temperature at the two ends of each probe.

The astronauts, however, will have to be careful not to put the probes anywhere near a crater, for craters create all sorts of temperature anomalies underground and could thus throw off the measurements. The astronauts have to carry a small white square box from the central station, unreeling the flat white wire behind it, and then unreel two more wires that lead from the box to the probes.

Far and away the most complicated job that any of the Apollo astronauts will have to perform in connection with laying out the ALSEP is drilling the two holes, and they are reluctant to take on the job at all. In fact, they scotched a scheme to gather a ten-foot underground core sample at the same time as they were drilling the holes for the heat probes. (The drilling may not be as difficult as the astronauts think, in the opinion of Thomas Gold, of Cornell, a selenologist who believes the moon may be covered by a fine powder. He said recently that the surface of the moon may be so soft that the holes could be dug in an instant with one poke of a crowbar. The human-factors engineers and Dr. Langseth, however, have agreed that the best way to drill a hole in the moon is by using a tungsten bit with five sharp teeth; tungsten is a tough, heat-resistant material that is often used for drilling holes on earth.) One astronaut will carry the drill and the heat probes, which together weigh twenty-six pounds—just over four pounds on the moon—to a smooth, craterless area, the drill and the bit in his right hand and the rest in his left. The drill rod will be broken down into sections, each one twenty-one inches long. Since he cannot reach lower than twenty-two inches from the ground, he will have to start by putting two of the drill sections together, making one piece forty-two inches long. The lower end of each section tapers just enough to slip tightly into the top of the section below it, so that as the drill, which is a percussive one, jounces up and down, the fit between the sections gets steadily tighter. As each section of the drill disappears into the ground, the astronaut will have to unscrew the motor from the top section and attach the next section, finally replacing the motor at the top. According to Dr. Langseth of the Lamont-Doherty Geological Laboratory, who designed the drill, this is about the only time that harm could befall an astronaut during the drilling: It is possible that the astronaut might get a finger stuck inside the hollow drill, which is an inch in diameter at the top of each section. Dr. Langseth says that he himself once caught a finger in the drill; however, he wasn't wearing thick space-suit gloves at the time. Dr. Langseth once watched Lind practice with the drill. All the while, human-factors engineers were offering advice like "If you pick up that section with your right hand instead of your left, you'll twist into a pretzel." Even with the human-factors men following every movement, Lind never *did* turn into a pretzel. Astronauts are notable for how quickly they pick up new ways of doing things. Dr. Langseth was impressed by the ease with which Lind got about in his cumbersome space suit. "Watching Lind, in his space suit, wielding the drill was like watching a very graceful elephant doing a dance," he says. "An elephant can't afford to make any false moves, and neither can an astronaut." (Lind said later that he felt less like a graceful elephant than like a clumsy deep-sea diver trying to repair a watch.) Teaching the astronauts how to use the drill is entirely in the hands of the human-factors engineers—a situation that nettles Dr. Langseth, even though he recognizes that the drill probably has more human-factors problems than any other part of the ALSEP. "I'd just like to *talk* to the astronauts and try to instill in them a little enthusiasm for this particular experiment," he says. The astronauts on the moon will have the final say about whether or not an experiment is done, and Dr. Langseth is afraid that they might decide at the last minute not to do the drilling and go on to some less time-consuming task instead.

Dr. Langseth had good reason to admire the way Lind wielded his drill, for Dr. Langseth had a rough time of it one day when he tried out an early model of the drill in a tubful of crushed Palisades basalt, which he uses to simulate the substance that the astronauts will be drilling into on the moon. Upon trying to pull the ten-foot drill out of the completed hole, he found that it had become wedged in. After exertions that would tax the cooling system of any space suit, he finally succeeded in extricating it, only to find that bits of basalt fell down inside the hole, partly plugging it up. He subsequently redesigned the drill so that it can be left in place in the ground. The sections of the drill will be made out of a tough dark-green plastic that is a very poor conductor of heat and therefore will not interfere with the heat-flow measurements. When the holes are finished, the astronaut will simply drop the heat probes down inside the drills.

While the astronauts are laying out the ALSEP, the scientists who designed the experiments, and who will have the first crack at analyzing the data they return—NASA calls them principal investigators—will be waiting in darkened rooms called Science-Support Rooms at the Mission Control Center watching the television screens and listening to every word the astronauts have to say about the positioning of their experiments, and ready to offer their advice if the need should arise. Dr. Langseth will be there, in case anything goes wrong with the drill. Another scientist who will be there is a dark-haired, wiry young geologist named Dr. Garry Latham, also of Lamont-Doherty, who is the principal investigator for the passive seismic experiment; he will be paying close attention as the astronauts report the emplacement of the round canister on its stool, the leveling of the experiment, and the careful unfolding of the Mylar shroud on the ground around it. The precise position of the experiment, and the exact point of the dial at the top where the shadow falls, are important to Dr. Latham, because one of the things he hopes to measure is any movement of the experiment caused by the tilt in the surface of the moon which is the result of the pull of the earth and the sun. The tidal bulges that the earth and the moon cause on one another pass not only through the oceans of the earth but also through the rocky crusts of both bodies and Dr. Latham is expecting to find that the passive seismometer moves back and forth one or two seconds of arc as the earth moves back and forth overhead—a prediction based on the hypothetical model of the moon that Dr. Latham believes is accurate. Dr. Latham is very anxious that the tidal tilt not be interfered with by the expansion and contraction of the ground as the temperature rises and falls, and that is why he wants the astronauts to lay the Mylar skirt around the experiment. Dr. Latham has spent years at Lamont-Doherty working out the experiment, during which he has tried to get some idea how much of a factor these changes of temperature will be by alternately heating and cooling a bed of perlite, a gravelly mineral that he feels resembles the surface of the moon. (It is quite different from Dr. Langseth's crushed Palisades basalt.)

The main purpose of the seismometer is the detection not of tilts but of moonquakes and meteor impacts. It is not certain that there are any moonquakes, though Dr. Latham says he will miss his guess if the passive seismic experiment records none. (In the event that there are no quakes, the astronauts are prepared to make some. The astronauts on one of the later flights may set up a small mortar on the moon. It won't be fired for a year, though, lest a stray shell blow up other ALSEP experiments. NASA also wants to crash some discarded rocket boosters onto the moon to see what kind of shock waves *they* will make.) The possibility of moonquakes—natural ones, that is—is tied up with the whole question of vulcanism and whether the moon possesses a hot, liquid core. There is thought to be *some* vulcanism on the moon, and where there is vulcanism there may also be quakes. There seems to be evidence of faulting—fracturing and slipping of the underlying rock—on the moon. At the moment, however, so little is known about the moon that Dr. Latham's preconceived model of it leaves up in the air the question of whether there is a hot, liquid core at all. Many selenologists, including Dr. Latham, incline to the view that there may be at least a very small one. (Dr. Urey has raised the possibility that there may be several separate "cores"—which he calls mass-concentrations, or mascons—scattered through the moon like raisins through a cake—a suggestion that was given some weight in December, when aberrations in the orbit of Apollo 8 indicated that the interior of the moon might be lumpy.) Recording seismic waves is one of the best means of finding out, for the manner in which waves come through the moon from its far side can tell not only whether there is a core or not but also how big the core is. If enough waves from enough different parts of the moon are recorded, the core (or cores) will cast a sort of shadow. However, in order to plot a seismograph shadow, it is essential to know exactly where moonquakes occur—knowledge that can be had with accuracy only by comparing the readings of two or more seismometers. Dr. Latham hopes to have a network of passive seismic experiments set up all over the moon, and his experiments will be carried in all the ALSEP's. Since NASA wants to have three landings a year for the next three or four years, until all the LM's are used up (though they may not in fact get that many), and since the life of each ALSEP is about a year, Dr. Latham hopes to have three of his experiments in working condition at least part of the time during that period. "Ideally, I would like to find seismic events on the moon, and find them occurring in such large numbers and at such high intensity that we'll be able to plot the structure of the moon right away," Dr. Latham said recently upon being asked what was the most that could be expected from the first crop of passive seismic experiments. Such a wealth of waves is unlikely, at best. Precise knowledge of the core of the moon (if one exists) will require many seismic readings over a long period, and much of the data they yield can be interpreted only by being run through computers. As the information comes in, Dr. Latham will have to keep adjusting his model of the moon to fit the new facts.

Selenologists work with mathematical models in the same way that chemists, physicists, and biologists do, refining them further as information comes in to narrow the possibilities. As all the data from the various ALSEP experiments are interrelated, and ultimately have to fit into the same model, the scientists' work becomes a little like doing a cryptogram; that is, as one set of facts becomes known, it limits the number of possible answers to the remaining unknowns. For example, if the passive seismic experiment should reveal the existence of a core, and if the magnetometer should show that the moon has a magnetic field, this combination of results would indicate that the core probably consisted in large part of iron—knowledge that might put a limit on what other metals were there. The magnetometer would also be measuring a magnetic field brought from the vicinity of the sun to the moon by the solar wind, the stream of particles always radiating away from the sun; and depending upon how this magnetic field flowed through, or around, the moon, the scientists might get a further line on the core. A molten core would distort the sun's magnetic field, possibly preventing it from passing through the moon at all, but if there were no core, the field would pass freely through it—information the magnetometer could obtain by comparing readings at noon with readings at the lunar midnight, when the instrument would be in a position to measure the sun's magnetic field coming *out* of the moon. The solar wind experiment would have a bearing on the core, for if it measured no solar wind at all, it could mean that the core is sufficiently large and molten to set up a magnetic field of its own high above the moon, shielding the surface from the solar wind—which is the case on earth. "By comparing information from all the experiments, we can probably infer a lot of things," Dr. Langseth says. The information on tidal tilt furnished by the passive seismic experiment is also relevant, for the manner in which the moon bulges under the gravitational pull of the earth ultimately depends on what the moon is made of and how it is put together. Among the more important experiments affecting the model are Dr. Langseth's four-foot heat probes. Dr. Langseth may find the temperature slightly higher at the bottom of the probes than at the top, for such a finding would indicate that heat was radiating away from the hypothetical core. If this proves to be the case, Dr. Langseth says, the precise curve of the change of temperature along the probe will give further definition to the size, the structure, and the composition of the hypothetical core. The heat-flow curve (if there is one) is an accurate index key to the interior of the moon, for not many sets of circumstances can lead to exactly that result. If Dr. Langseth's estimate of the core, based on heat flow, doesn't initially coincide with Dr. Latham's, based on seismic waves, the reason they don't will be of interest to both men. Local variations, such as an underground rock layer, could throw both experiments off. However, so little is known about the moon that either scientist might be quite content to discover even an underground layer of rock. In any event, both of them are certain that our knowledge of the moon will catch up relatively quickly with our knowledge of the earth, because the instruments that are available to selenologists today are far more precise than any that geologists had until recently; Dr. Langseth says that, given the smaller size of the moon, it is altogether possible that we will eventually know *more* about its interior than we do about the earth's. It will take some years to process the information, however. To the principal investigators, the most useful instruments will be some that are deployed not on the moon but in various basements on earth. The ALSEP will be pumping back so many bits of data per second that Dr. Latham says he will be spending most of his time at a computer after the astronauts have put his first passive seismic experiment in place. Some of the computers are so sophisticated that they can take the data from the ALSEP and project upon a sort of television screen a picture of what the moon is actually like.

After the astronauts have deployed the ALSEP, but before Dr. Latham can get cracking with his computer, someone at the Mission Control Center in Houston will flip a switch, turning the ALSEP generator on and starting the experiments. If the switch in Houston doesn't work, the astronauts can turn the ALSEP on themselves. The astronauts may feel like men who have spent a long time decorating a particularly challenging Christmas tree at the moment that the lights are turned on. Turning on the ALSEP, however, will not be nearly as dramatic, for nothing lights up and nothing moves, except for the sensors of the magnetometer, which may occasionally rotate. If anything is wrong with the equipment, there isn't much that the astronauts, with their thick gloves, will be able to do about it—though there have been times when even a thickly padded helping hand could have made the difference between success and failure of the equipment in some of our satellites. The most sophisticated electronic equipment can sometimes benefit from a thump in the right place—a fundamental non-human factor that the experimenters on earth might be glad to avail themselves of while the astronauts are still on the moon. The astronauts could certainly tighten any loose connections where the flat white wires plug into the central station. After the passive seismic experiment is operating, Dr. Latham may want a little fine adjustment of its position. Then the astronauts will start back to the LM —first tossing the universal handling tool, which they won't need anymore, across the black *mare*, where it may skitter to rest inside a small crater.

The LM will be a spidery black and silver tower a hundred yards away from the weblike ALSEP—about a third of the distance to the skyline. (Although it weighs sixteen tons and stands almost twenty-three feet tall, the LM is delicate looking. Seen from head on, the ascent stage looks almost human. For no apparent reason, the front of the ascent stage looks exactly like a huge mechanical face with a somewhat elfin expression—the surreptitious handiwork, perhaps, of an artistic Grumman gremlem. The two windows and a riding light between them look like eyes and nose while on either side small jets stick out like ears. The mouth—the hatch—is wide with surprise, as if the LM were alarmed to find itself on the moon. In designing a totally new object to carry them onto a new planet, men had, perhaps unconsciously, made it in their own familiar image.) As the astronauts walk toward it, their feet may drag a bit, for Schmitt and Lind agree that a pair of astronauts who have set up the ALSEP will be utterly exhausted. Inside the LM, though, they will have a lot to do before they can knock off and rest. First, they will have to close the hatch and build up the oxygen pressure in the cabin, so that they can take off their Lexan bubble helmets. The helmets will go into two bags that look like bags for bowling balls; the astronauts' gloves go in the bag with the helmets. The men will not take off their suits while they are on the moon, but, with the helmets off, the pressure inside will be released and they will also be able to move more freely. They will be able to talk to each other without radios, though their voices will be higher-pitched than on earth because the atmospheric pressure in the LM is about a third what it is on earth. Next, the astronauts will have to check out the LM and report its condition to Houston. For any number of reasons, they may feel they've had enough, and decide to head for home at this point, leaving the geological field trip for other astronauts. However, if they stay on, they will have their dinner and then they will try to get some sleep. According to one schedule, six hours and seven minutes have been allotted to "sleep and rest." Lind says, "My bet is they'll conk right out. Three hours in a pressure suit is a day's work for anyone." It may not be so easy. A number of discomforts may stand between the astronauts and their sleep. To begin with, the LM isn't very comfortable; neither man will be able to stretch out. One astronaut will prop himself near the forward hatch, beneath the main dashboard, and the other will curl up on top of the ascent-stage engine, which protrudes through the floor in the rear of the cabin. However, Schmitt, who is short and supple, doesn't believe that all this will interfere with sleeping, on the theory that sitting in the moon's one-sixth gravity is the equivalent of lying down on earth, in that it will take next to no effort. Yet, even assuming that the astronauts can make themselves comfortable enough to sleep, there is no assurance that they will actually be able to do so. Anxiety has plagued many an astronaut in science fiction. Among insomniac astronauts is Mr. Bedford, in "The First Men in the Moon," who, shortly before he takes off for the moon from the marshy downs around Lympne, in Kent, spends a sleepless night. "I don't think I ever had such a night," he writes:

> I was suddenly in the most enormous funk of the thing we were going to do. I do not remember before that night thinking at all of the risks we were running. Now they came like that array of spectres that once beleagured Prague, and camped around me. The strangeness of what we were [doing], the unearthliness of it, overwhelmed me. I was like a man awakened out of pleasant dreams to the most horrible surroundings. I lay, eyes wide open; and the [spaceship] seemed to get more flimsy and feeble . . . and the whole enterprise madder and madder, every moment.

The No. 1 funk-making question for the Apollo astronauts will be whether the LM will get off the moon. If the ignition system, for example, doesn't work, and the astronauts are unable to fix it, nothing could be done for them. There are no plans to send spare parts to the moon—to have Surveyors, for instance, perched on landing pads to act as unmanned trouble wagons delivering new batteries to the astronauts, or a special wrench they might need. Such a Surveyor couldn't reach the moon before the LM's forty-eight-hour supply of oxygen ran out. (The astronauts will have no provision for suicide, such as the U-2 pilots had, but an astronaut stranded on the moon could forestall a lingering death simply by stepping outside the LM and removing his helmet.) Nonetheless, the astronauts would regard Bedford, with his spectres of Prague, as a nervous Nellie. A young engineer at the M.S.C. recently said admiringly, "The astronauts don't blow their cool. They're very calm. Very practical. They're just cool customers, boy!" (The astronauts do their best to keep this super-cool image going, and possibly the coolest thing an astronaut ever did was Gordon Cooper's feat of going to sleep on the launching pad during a hold in a countdown at Cape Kennedy.) To Schmitt it is virtually unthinkable that the fragile, spidery LM won't get off the moon. He is sure of his sleep because "after landing we check the LM right off the bat, so there is a confidence factor going for us," he says, adding, "You see, we never initiate a phase until we know we can complete it." To a lesser mortal, a confidence factor such as this might seem a bit less than substantial. When it is suggested to Schmitt that some crucial part on the LM might blow after the next phase had been initiated and the astronauts were irretrievably on the moon, he says simply, "Well, we are trained to carry out this kind of job under stress." Lind, who is every bit as unflappable as Schmitt, greets the suggestion that an astronaut might worry himself into a sleepless night with incredulity. His reasoning is somewhat *a posteriori.* "Sleeping is one of the important things we'll have to do," he says. "It's essential for longer missions. You can't stay keyed up for ten days." He adds conclusively, "Sleeping time is programmed into the schedule. When the astronauts settle down to it, they will sleep." Neither Schmitt nor Lind can conceive of anything else. If an astronaut wishes to stretch his legs during the time allotted for sleeping, about the best he can do will be to stand up, raise the Aclar blind over the window, and look out at the ALSEP, littering the ground in the middle distance like an abandoned campsite—the SIDE a rectangular charcoal grill with the cold-cathode gauge a matchbox nearby, and the passive seismic experiment sitting on its round skirt like an overturned carton of ice cream from which a melting puddle is creeping outward. The experiments will stand out white against the black *mare*, and the *mare* itself will be starting to blanch as the blazing sun moves slowly toward the zenith, which it will reach some six days later —a couple of days, the restless astronaut may reflect, after he gets home. "Home" will be hovering tantalizingly overhead, like a blue balloon caught in the treetops.

PART III
Exploring

Beginning possibly with the second Apollo landing, the two astronauts will leave the LM a second time in order to go on an extended geological field trip, which most astronauts expect will be the most rewarding part of the stay on the moon. By the time they start out on the field trip, they will have been on the moon some twelve or fifteen hours, during which time they will have been outside the spacecraft for less than three hours. Having woken up from their rest period following the deployment of the ALSEP, they will check out the LM to make sure that all is well with it, and after that they will don their clear Lexan helmets with the golden sun shades, depressurize the spacecraft, and slither down the LM's ladder. Once again they will be standing on the blackish *mare.* They will promptly set about preparing for the field trip, which will last two hours or so. Unlike the ALSEP instruments, which are designed primarily to peer deep inside the moon, the field trip has as its purpose the skimming of information and material from the surface. The field trip will be the high point of the visit not only for the astronauts, who will now have a chance to see what they can do on their own, but for a majority of the selenologists back on earth as well. During the excursion, which could cover as much as two kilometres, the astronauts will gather as many as two hundred samples of rocks and dirt, carefully describing and cataloguing each. These samples, which together may weigh as much as sixty-five pounds (but less than eleven pounds on the moon), will later be distributed to one hundred and forty geologists, biologists, chemists, and physicists around the world, possibly including some in Communist nations. The samples will be the most tangible result of the journey, providing the most direct information about what the moon is like. When they are brought back, the hundred-odd scientists will submit the samples to extremely close scrutiny. At the moment, however, so little is known about the moon that the observations of almost anybody with a sharp pair of eyes would answer a lot of questions. Consequently, selenology is at the moment the most speculative, and most prickly, subject on earth.

The issue that is most apt to raise the hackles of selenologists is whether the craters of the moon were formed primarily by meteors crashing into the moon at high speeds or by volcanic activity. This argument is closely allied to another, about whether the moon has a hot, liquid core, for if there is a good deal of vulcanism, the moon would have to have a molten center—or, possibly, a number of sizable pockets of molten material scattered through its interior. Settling the argument about what formed the craters is important, because craters may well be the commonest topographical feature of all the planets that have solid surfaces. A few years ago, Mariner IV sent back photographs showing that Mars is pocked with craters, like the moon, and there is reason to believe that the earth may once have been pocked with them, too. Therefore, finding out what formed the craters is important to an understanding of the entire solar system. The craters on the moon range in diameter from a few inches to a hundred and sixty miles, and possibly much, much more. Regardless of their size, they are shallow depressions, like saucers, with rubbly rims that are slightly higher than the surrounding ground, and the larger craters frequently have in the center a rocky pinnacle called the central peak. Most non-selenologists automatically incline to the view that the craters were made by meteors, for it is almost impossible to look at the moon without thinking that it has been smashed into millions of times. From the earth, the moon looks like a target range for heavy artillery. Plenty of selenologists are of the same opinion, though their theory has it, more scientifically, that meteors are constantly crashing into the moon's surface at speeds of up to thirty miles a second, fast enough so that the energy of motion is converted suddenly into heat, and the heat turns the meteor and the ground around it into gas, which expands and explodes with a force equal to that of an atomic bomb. Consequently, these selenologists maintain, the craters are vastly bigger than the meteors that made them, just as rings in the water are bigger than the pebbles that caused them. Impact men like to compare craters to rings in the water, because such circular ripples often have central peaks the way the craters have. When a pebble hits the water, the waves first surge out and then surge back, splashing up in the center; similarly, after a meteoric impact, molten rock may surge outward and then back, so that some of it flies up at the center and hardens. Vulcanists, who take a dim view of the ripple theory, say that the craters are calderas. On earth, calderas are the product of a sometimes relatively gentle form of volcanic activity. Not far below the surface, a pocket of magma, or molten rock, forms, making a round blister called a pluton; when the magma drains away through an underground passage, the ground above it caves in, forming a circular crater. Vulcanists say that the central peak in a lunar crater is magma that solidified at the top of the duct that drained the pluton. The reason that selenologists bicker so much about the craters is that they explain most of the other features of the moon in terms of either impact or vulcanism. For instance, the impact men say that the circular *maria,* such as the Mare Imbrium, the Mare Serenitatis, and the Mare Crisium, which are hundreds of miles across, are gigantic craters, whereas the vulcanists say that they are a heavy volcanic rock in which the lighter highlands or continents are floating, as on earth. At present, there is a tendency for the two sides to come together a little, each side granting that both vulcanism and impact may have contributed to the formation of the features on the moon. Even so, selenologists can still wrangle over which force had the *greater* influence. They are currently arguing over individual craters as passionately as ever, each side staking its claim on as many craters as it can in a sort of lunar land rush. One of the astronauts who flew around the moon in Apollo 8 said later, "There are an awful lot of holes on the moon. I think there are enough for both theories." Indeed, in their uneasy truce some selenologists claim to see both forces at work in a single hole. For instance, some are now suggesting that the circular *maria* like the Mare Imbrium may have been made by a big meteor that hit the moon to make a crater as much as fifty miles deep and weakening the moon's crust so that lava flowed out through fissures from the molten interior to partly fill up the *mare* floor. Not all selenologists are so accommodating, however; there are still a few hard-core vulcanists—or, rather, soft-, *molten*-core vulcanists—who deny that any meteors ever hit the moon, maintaining that, rare as the moon's atmosphere may be, it is no rarer than the area high above this planet where earthbound meteors burn up.

Selenologists gather frequently at conventions, which are apt to be stormy. As the selenologists present their latest thinking about conditions on the moon, the astronauts are likely to listen in, and when this happens, the lectures bristle with hints about things that the astronauts should look for while they are on the field trip. One such gathering of selenologists was held at the Goddard Space Flight Center, at Greenbelt, Maryland, in the spring of 1965, and another—the forty-ninth annual meeting of the American Geophysical Union—was held at the Sheraton-Park Hotel in Washington last year. In the three-year interval between the conferences, five Lunar Orbiters had circled the moon and five Surveyors had successfully landed on it, and thousands of photographs had been returned by these spacecraft, and yet not a great deal more was known about the moon at the second meeting than at the first. The most important thing the photographs showed was that there is, beyond doubt, *some* vulcanism on the moon. The vulcanists, in fact, are fairly crowing over the photographs, in which can be seen, among other sulphurous items, many craters that are neatly centered on the tops of mountains. It is too much to believe, the vulcanists say, that these craters result from perfect hits scored by meteors on mountain peaks. Moreover, Surveyor V reported that the material on the surface of the *maria* resembles basalt, which is a volcanic rock, and the Lunar Orbiters photographed what look like lava flows. (So did the Apollo astronauts, last December.) Though some of the more extreme impact men have had to revise their position somewhat, the rest feel that theirs is still unassailable, for the presence of *some* vulcanism by no means invalidates their contention that the moon's surface was sculptured primarily by meteors. This feeling that matters hadn't changed so very much after all was expressed by Dr. Urey, professor (at-large) of chemistry at the University of California. In fact, Dr. Urey, an impact man, said at the meeting this spring, selenology hadn't changed appreciably in all the time he had been a selenologist. "Twenty years ago, I recognized that most of the craters of the moon were collisional, and some were plutonic, and we're *still* at that stage," he said. Dr. Urey, who is seventy-six, is the chemist who discovered heavy hydrogen back in the thirties. He explained once, "After the war, I was tired of doing secret work. Then I read a book by Ralph Baldwin about the moon—'The Face of the Moon'—and I've been an astronomer ever since." (Baldwin, who did most of his research in the early forties, was the first person to suggest convincingly that meteors might have made many of the moon's craters; previously, almost all selenologists had been vulcanists.) Besides Dr. Urey, the selenologists at the meeting this spring included Mr. Thomas Gold, professor of astronomy at Cornell; Dr. Eugene Shoemaker, of the California Institute of Technology and the Astrogeological Division of the United States Geological Survey, in Flagstaff, Arizona; Dr. Harold Masursky, also with the U.S.G.S., in Flagstaff; and Mr. Donald E. Gault and Dr. John O'Keefe, both with the National Aeronautics and Space Administration. The sides these men take are known to their colleagues. Dr. Urey, for example, is known for his belief that there was once water on the moon. (Proof of this theory is important to Dr. Urey, for the presence at one time or another of water on the moon would bolster his contention that the moon had once passed close enough to the earth to be splashed by its oceans.) At conventions, Dr. Urey is likely to buttonhole passing selenologists and tell them that a certain depression near the crater Alphonsus might be a dried-up lake bed or that a serpentine fissure running down Schröter's Valley, an arid canyon near the crater Aristarchus, could have been made only by a meandering river that has long since evaporated. Mr. Gold is known to believe that there may have been water on the moon, too, though he says that the water welled up from underground. In fact, he thinks there may still be water beneath the surface. Mr. Gold, who is one of the most outspoken impact men, is best known for a theory that he suggested many years ago. He said then that the moon may be covered by a deep layer of powder. Some selenologists say that Mr. Gold's deep dust was once several kilometres thick—certainly deep enough to swallow up any spacecraft—but Mr. Gold is now willing to settle for the idea of a thinner layer. He has residual fears, however, that the spacecraft might be swallowed up, and wants some procedure established to abort the landing if the ground gives way. (Mr. Gold's dust differs from the grit everyone knows is there in that it is finer grained and more powdery.) Mr. Gold is a tough-looking astronomer, whose ideas stretch beyond the moon to quasars and pulsars, and who has been known to espouse causes many feel are lost, such as the steady-state theory of the universe. Whenever he feels that one of his theories is being attacked, he defends it with loud argument delivered in a staccato British accent. (He was born in Vienna and studied in England, at Cambridge.) When he turns his attention to the moon, he is often at noisy loggerheads with Dr. O'Keefe, a mild-looking man who is a passionate champion of vulcanism. In fact, Mr. Gold is something of a professional gadfly. At the meeting this spring, all six of these men held a panel discussion, during which Schmitt, the astronaut, sat in the audience and jotted down an occasional note in his program.

The arguments started even before the panel discussion got going. Dr. Masursky, a dark-haired young selenologist, preceded it with a lecture, in which he compared photographs of certain volcanic features on earth with photographs of craters on the moon, the implication being that what had caused the former (vulcanism) had caused the latter. Mr. Gold, who has little patience with volcanoes, apparently couldn't wait for the panel discussion to begin; he let out an audible snort during the lecture, and when the lights came on he leaped to his feet to chastise Dr. Masursky for arguing by analogy. Dr. Masursky replied smoothly that he wasn't drawing conclusions—just showing slides. Shortly after this, the six selenologists mounted the platform together and sat in an uncomfortable row under the eye of Dr. Martin J. Swetnick, a NASA scientist, who was the moderator. The discussion got off to a slow, gentlemanly start, with each panelist saying a few words in turn. Occasionally, some of the suggestions put forward seemed as unlikely as the projects of the scientists in "Gulliver's Travels"—such as the member of the Grand Academy of Lagado who was engaged in extracting sunbeams from cucumbers. But since something of the sort will have to be done with a sheet of aluminum foil that the astronauts are to bring back from the moon in the hope that it will be teeming with particles from the solar wind, it may be that many of the ideas brought up at the meeting were not as unlikely as they sounded. One of the unlikeliest-sounding of all was advanced by Dr. O'Keefe, who was among the first to speak. Dr. O'Keefe, as a vulcanist, seemed nervous at finding himself amid a pack of impact men. He wanted to alter a theory he had long been associated with, he said—that tektites, unusual glassy beads of rock found on earth, had originally been hurled here from the moon, by the same volcanic explosions that caused the craters. He wished to concede the point that evidence from some of the Surveyors had shown that the chemical content of rocks in the *maria* was not the same as that of the tektites, and that his tektites therefore couldn't have come from these particular *maria*; however, they could still have come from other parts of the moon. (Schmitt scribbled a note—possibly reminding himself to keep an eye out for tektites on the moon.) Impact selenologists don't like Dr. O'Keefe's tektites, because they are a form of volcanic rock, and so, if it turned out that they did come from the moon, they would score a point for the vulcanists. Three years before, Dr. O'Keefe had held off a roomful of impact selenologists in a tumultuous argument that ended in something approaching an uproar; chief among Dr. O'Keefe's attackers in what amounted to a star-chamber inquisition had been Dr. Urey, for almost every time that Dr. O'Keefe cited a tektite that might have come from the moon, Dr. Urey managed to point out a crater on earth that the tektite could equally well have come from. This time, Dr. O'Keefe sat down without further incident, and Dr. Swetnick, the moderator, projected on a screen an Orbiter photograph showing a huge boulder that had evidently rolled some six hundred metres down a slope, leaving a series of depressions where it had bounced—marks rather like animal tracks in snow. Dr. Swetnick believed that the boulder had been initially dislodged by a moonquake, which would imply a good deal of volcanic activity in the area. Mr. Gold, who, as an impact man, may have felt that the boulder looming on the screen was aimed at him, dodged it by saying immediately that what interested *him* about the photograph was not how the boulder had been dislodged but, rather, the depth of the depressions that the boulder had made in the lunar hillside, for these indicated that the dust in some places was quite deep. (Schmitt took another note.) Mr. Gold's deep-dust theory had run into trouble, because all five of the Surveyor spacecraft, far from sinking out of sight, had sunk only about one to two inches. Consequently, Mr. Gold was on the lookout for deep dust wherever he could find it. He still refuses to abandon his deep dust, suggesting that even in places where Surveyors stay stubbornly afloat on the surface the explanation may be that the dust has compacted into a layer a few millimetres thick. Then Mr. Gault, another impact man, rose to put in a few words for the possibility that the circular *maria,* such as the Mare Imbrium, which is about the same size as France and England combined, are enormous meteor craters. One of the vulcanists presented the familiar suggestion that the lunar *maria* were of heavier volcanic rock than the highlands, as is the situation with the ocean basins on earth, but Mr. Gault countered with the proposition that the ocean basins on *earth* might have been made by huge meteoric impacts, too. This was too much for Dr. O'Keefe, who half rose to protest, but the impact men were off and running. Mr. Gold talked of groups of islands in our oceans that form rings or parts of rings, such as the long arc of the Caribbean islands, asking poetically, "Could they be imprints of impact craters deep on the ocean floor, their underlying circularity shining through?" Dr. O'Keefe, who was not to be put off by a neatly turned phrase, and whose underlying annoyance was decidedly shining through, launched a flank attack on Mr. Gold. Mr. Gold had once said there was ice just below the surface of the moon, but Dr. O'Keefe had recently thought of a reason that this couldn't be so. He sprang his reason now. Since ice is a viscous substance, and flows, as in glaciers, he argued, then any sheet of ice underlying the *maria* would flow, thereby smoothing and obliterating the surface features above it. However, the surface features have not been obliterated, and so, he concluded, there can be no ice under the moon. This reasoning reminded one listener of the man at the Grand Academy of Lagado who built houses from the roof down, and Mr. Gold, who can be a ferocious huffer and puffer, proceeded to blow the house down in the same manner. He shouted, "That's why I keep saying the ice layer is a layer of permafrost! I don't expect to find a whole damn lake down there! However, there *are* smooth areas of the moon, where there are one one-hundredths the number of craters that other areas have, and perhaps there are frozen lakes under them!" Dr. O'Keefe looked crushed; Mr. Gold sat down triumphantly; and Dr. Urey took the floor to give Dr. O'Keefe a few more reasons that his tektites could not have come from the moon. Mr. Gold, however, met his comeuppance shortly afterward, when the panelists adjourned to another room to hold a press conference. At the conference, Dr. O'Keefe looked dejected, for Dr. Urey was on one side of him and Mr. Gold on the other. On either side of *them,* however, were Dr. Shoemaker and Dr. Masursky, and Dr. Masursky, it turned out, had been quietly biding his time since his exchange with Mr. Gold about volcanoes. At one point, Mr. Gold was telling a reporter about a theory he had formulated to the effect that his fine powder was transported about the moon on an electrostatic charge that many scientists believe hovers just above the surface. Dr. Masursky suddenly pounded the table and shouted, "Electrostatic transportation doesn't exist!" Mr. Gold retorted that selenologists had all believed that the moon was solid rock until he suggested that there might be dust on it, and that shortly they would come around to believing in electrostatic transportation, too, whereupon Dr. Shoemaker shouted, "We all thought the moon had dust on it twenty years ago!" Dr. Shoemaker, who is in charge of analyzing the Surveyor photographs, often has the last word at conferences, and he had it this time, for the meeting almost immediately broke up in an uproar. In the mid-twentieth century it is unusual to find a field in which the top men are in such radical disagreement about its basic facts, the way biologists were about evolution in the nineteenth—or selenologists were in the seventeenth, when Galileo suggested that there might be mountains on the moon and wound up in prison. If the astronauts accomplish nothing else on their field trip, they may calm some nerves by settling some disputes. Schmitt could make Dr. O'Keefe very happy if he found rocks identical to tektites during his lunar walk, and Mr. Gold would be in seventh heaven if Schmitt or any other astronaut found some specks of powder floating above a crater.

Dr. Urey has said that he hopes the astronauts will land in the Oceanus Procellarum, an irregular *mare* about as big as the Mediterranean, that runs from the center clear to the western edge of the side of the moon that faces the earth. (The western edge is on the lower left as the moon rises.) From the earth, the Oceanus Procellarum, which is the largest of all the *maria*, looks like the rough, patchy body of a bear, with the round Mare Imbrium making the bear's head. (A small, round *mare*, the Sinus Iridium, and a large crater, Plato, both to the north of the Mare Imbrium, make the bear's ears.) At the bear's shoulder is Copernicus, a huge crater with long rays separating the Mare Imbrium from the Oceanus Procellarum. In this vast area is Site 4, the second most westerly of five Apollo landing sites chosen by NASA. The target moves one site to the west, following the sun across the face of the moon, each time a launching is put off. The five sites look so much alike from the earth that some selenologists feel the astronauts might just as well land at one as at another. Colonel Frank Borman, the commander of the Apollo 8 flight around the moon, feels that the same thing could be said of virtually any spot on the moon. "I came away with the idea that you could [dig] a spoon [in any] place and find it just about the same as the samples somewhere else," he reported at a press conference after he got back. Dr. Urey disagrees. "I hope that Apollo doesn't get off the first day, when the target is in the Mare Tranquillitatis, or the second day, when the target is in the Sinus Medii," he has said. "I hope it gets off the third day and goes to the Oceanus Procellarum. Oceanus Procellarum is different from the other *maria* —parts of it are blacker—and I'd be interested to know why." Assuming that the astronauts, having awakened from their sleep, are standing once more on the black *mare,* they will, according to Dr. John W. Dietrich, a geologist at the M.S.C., "observe a generally smooth horizon interrupted only by irregularities associated with small craters that are rarely larger than six hundred feet across." In his outline of what the astronauts will see, Dr. Dietrich thoughtfully converted the metric system into feet, yards, and miles, for the benefit of the layman. "For a six-foot man, the distance to the horizon on a perfect spheroid the size of the moon would be one and four-tenths miles, but surface irregularities could restrict the horizon distance to a thousand yards or less," he went on. "Isolated hills up to thirteen hundred feet high that are twenty-two to thirty miles west of the site may project above the horizon if the landing occurs near the western margin of the site. Groups of hills thirty to thirty-six miles south-southwest of the landing site will not be visible above the horizon although they rise to elevations as great as two thousand three hundred feet above the surrounding area." Dr. Dietrich's assumption was that the astronauts would have landed in the middle of the site, which is an imaginary oval five miles long and three miles wide, and under those circumstances they would see no mountains whatever; instead, they would be standing in the center of a flat black pancake containing bubbles formed by craters. In this nondescript landscape, the nearest landmark big enough to have a name is a crater a mile or so across known as Wickmann CA, which is out of sight fifteen miles to the north. Dr. Dietrich, a partly bald man with rugged features, says gloomily that geologists ordinarily prefer more varied country, but that it will be a long time before spacecraft land on parts of the moon other than the *maria*—though later Apollo missions may land within walking distance of such relatively interesting features as rilles, ridges, and large craters. Landing in the moon's highlands won't take place for some time at least, and it may be that the highlands can be best explored by astronauts who land in the *maria* and travel to the highlands by other means. The other means that NASA is now thinking of include a truck with enormous pillow-like tires (the Local Scientific Survey Module) and a rocket-powered gadget that is still in the design stage (the Lunar Flying Unit). In the meantime, the astronauts must be content to explore the *maria*. One person who is far from content with this situation is Mr. Gold, for he doubts whether manned landings in what amounts to a lunar parking lot will have much value. "The landing site is deliberately selected to be uninteresting," he complains. "It will be as if a group of Martians landed in the Sahara, scooped up some sand, and went back to Mars thinking they knew about the earth." However, it is possible that even Sahara sand would be of interest to the first Martians to reach the earth. And even Mr. Gold isn't uninterested in the *maria*. At the conference last spring, he was standing in a red-carpeted corridor at the Sheraton-Park Hotel, telling Dr. Urey and Dr. Alan Cameron, a tall, broad-shouldered selenologist in a gray suit, that the *maria* were doubtless rich in iron, at least on the surface, and that if this indeed proved to be the case, the explanation was very likely a blend of two theories that Mr. Gold is fond of—the impact theory and the theory of electrostatic transportation of particles. If, as he suggests, the iron on the surface of the *maria* came originally from meteors, the entire moon should be covered with iron-rich debris, and not just the *maria* alone. (Mr. Gold talks of the iron-rich layer as being not very thick because he thinks that iron-rich meteors are relatively recent in the solar system, by which he means that they are younger at least than the moon itself, which is thought to be four and one-half billion years old.) Unlike the *maria*, the moon's highlands are thought to be relatively poor in iron; if they in fact are, this would seem to be at variance with the idea that iron-rich meteors have been landing evenly all over the moon. Mr. Gold thinks that he has the answer—his theory of electrostatic transportation, which suggests that craters can be filled by particles of dust that are kicked up by meteorites and then slide down Mr. Gold's electrostatic charge until the crater is choked and even obliterated. In similar fashion, Mr. Gold suggested, particles of iron from meteors have moved from the highlands down onto the *maria*—which are possibly the biggest craters of all—so that they have become the repositories for most of the iron on the surface of the moon. Dr. Urey said this sounded like an interesting thought. Dr. Cameron, however, disagreed, saying that meteors are also rich in magnesium, but that since it has not yet been established that the *maria* are richer in that metal, too, it would be wise to wait until the relative magnesium content of the highlands and *maria* is known. There the matter dropped, until the astronauts embard upon their field trip on the *mare* floor.

Before the astronauts leave the LM, they will spend some time plotting a route for the field trip. From there, they ought to be able to see about three miles. They will have to give the terrain a closer look than before. Its most noticeable feature will be the incredible number of small craters. An astronomer on earth looking at the moon through a telescope finds that as he doubles the magnification, the number of craters he sees is doubled, too. NASA has doubled and redoubled the highest telescopic magnification of the moon by means of the Lunar Orbiter spacecraft, which, bringing the moon to within a few miles, have revealed craters as small as two feet across. A good many selenologists are beginning to think that the myriad little craters were made by meteors because it is hard to account in any other fashion for the way they pepper the ground. Seen from an Orbiter, Site 4 looks like a clay tennis court that has been rolled flat and has then been pelted by raindrops during a short, hard cloudburst; some of the larger craters (the largest ones in the Lunar Orbiter photographs are six hundred metres across) look like puddles. When Dr. Dietrich puts a magnifying glass over the center of the site photograph, raising the power again, he can get a fairly good idea of what the astronauts will see. Standing in the LM, they will feel as if they were on a raft in the middle of a glassy black lake where raindrops were just beginning to fall—the myriad small craters being about the size of the rings that raindrops make in the water. (The bigger craters will be another matter.) In some places the ground will roll slightly, suggesting a gentle swell. As with rings in the water, some of the craters will be more clearly defined than others. The craters with the sharpest outlines are presumably the youngest. Selenologists call the comparatively faint, older craters "subdued," rather than, say, "weathered," in order to sidestep the tricky question of erosion on the moon. Some are so subdued that they have all but disappeared into the *mare* floor, like the last ripply trace of a ring in the water. Some geologists rate craters on an age scale of one through eight, No. 8 craters being the youngest and therefore as a rule the sharpest, while No. 1's are the oldest and usually the most subdued. There aren't many soft, old No. 1's where the astronauts are looking, nor are there many sharp, young No. 8's, because the area around youthful No. 8's is apt to be strewn with jagged, chunky blocks, which the astronauts will have avoided. There will, however, be a good deal of rubble. The rubble will be strewn in and between the craters, and there will be larger concentrations of it in the vicinity of the larger craters. The rubble is thought to be mostly rocks that look like New England fieldstones, but no such stones show up in the Orbiter photographs of

Site 4; this means that any stones there are smaller than two feet across—which is one reason the site was chosen. Dr. Dietrich nonetheless has reason to believe that rubble is present, for such rocks show up in Surveyor photographs taken on the ground in other *maria*. Similarly, there may be a few No. 8 craters that are too small to show up on the photographs.

In plotting the route for their field trip, the astronauts will probably want to go out to the farthest point first and work their way back, so that the longer they are out, the nearer they will be to the LM, in case any trouble develops with their life-support systems. There is enough oxygen in the backpacks they will wear to last four hours, so, in their trip of three hours, there is a one-hour leeway in their oxygen supply. Going to the farthest point first and then working back will also prevent the astronauts from wandering farther and farther from the LM as they go from one point of interest to another, and perhaps getting too far away to get back at all. With his magnifying glass and photograph, Dr. Dietrich has plotted out a route that would interest him, were he an astronaut who had landed in the center of Site 4. He would go first to a field of small craters about one-half of a kilometre, or three-tenths of a mile, southwest of the LM; then to a large crater about a fourth of a kilometre, or 1.5 tenths of a mile, to the north; and then back to the LM, possibly taking in some smaller craters on the way. The route is roughly triangular, with the first leg—the one from the LM to the crater field—the longest; after the crater field, to which he would go as directly as possible, everything else would be more or less on the way back to the LM.

This trip would be a kilometre and a quarter long, but detours would be bound to lengthen it to perhaps two kilometres; there are too many craters to walk in a straight line. Although the astronauts are capable of walking about three kilometres an hour on the moon, even in their cumbersome space suits, Dr. Dietrich feels that the trip he has planned may be too ambitious for the astronauts in view of the constant stops they will be making. Because they have two hundred Teflon bags to fill, they will be stopping frequently.

When the astronauts start out on the first leg of the journey, toward the crater field three-quarters of a kilometre to the southwest, one of them will be carrying a set of geological hand tools in a triangular rack, and the other will have a camera. There is only one set of geological tools, for while one astronaut is gathering geological samples, the other will be taking photographs and generally keeping a sharp eye on things. The human-factors engineers have worked very hard on the geological tools, for conditions on the moon demand special modifications. All the tools are made of aluminum alloys or stainless steel and look white or silvery. Among them are a geologist's hammer; a scoop; a small weighing scale; some small tubes for gathering core samples; a surveying instrument consisting of a compass, a range finder, and a scale for inclination; and a device that acts as a plumb line. There is also a small tool that combines a magnifying glass, a brush for sweeping dust from a sample, and a hard point for scratching an identifying number on a sample. About the only tool that the astronauts will have in addition to the tools used by a geologist on earth is a pair of tongs for picking up interesting-looking rocks; the tongs are needed because, in their space suits, the astronauts cannot bend over far enough to touch the ground. There is also a long extension handle, for lengthening the reach of the scoop and the hammer; the tools themselves are all quite short, to make them more compact. The rack and the tools fit together ingeniously. The tools are ranged horizontally up the outside of two sides of the rack, the third side being a sort of gate which permits the rack to be folded flat for stowing aboard the LM. On the field trip, the rack will be opened out horizontally into a triangle that can stand safely on the ground, and suspended in its center there will be a big Teflon sack to hold the samples. The human-factors engineers have worried about the rack almost as much as they worried about the universal handling tool, the special implement designed for setting up the ALSEP. Before the Surveyor landings, when many selenologists thought that the floors of the *maria* might be a good deal more rugged than they are, human-factors engineers felt that the astronauts, already tippy inside their ballooning space suits, could use a bit more in the way of stablization. Accordingly, they designed a big, five-sided device a little like the temporary pipe-frame fences that Con Ed puts around manholes in the city; an astronaut would have stood inside this and used it as a lame person uses a walker, and the tools would have hung on the outside. However, the astronauts, who want all the freedom they can get, took a dim view of the device, and, accordingly, it was scotched.

Before gathering their first sample, the astronauts will walk out a hundred feet or so from the LM, to avoid getting samples contaminated by fumes from the spacecraft. Since every bit of the moon's crust will be new to them, and to the scientists back on earth, there may be a tendency at the start to stop at almost every step to scoop dust out of a tiny crater or to pick up a curious pebble with the tongs. The easiest sample to gather will be the dust, for it will be all about them—black, fine-grained, and cohesive. They may feel as if they were standing in a desert of graphite powder. Some impact men say that it may be a blanket of pulverized moon rock shattered by the billions of meteors that have smashed into the moon like (as one Apollo 8 astronaut radioed back) "pickaxes striking concrete, creating a lot of fine haze dust"—a theory that can be checked if the astronauts bring some dust home. They will peer appraisingly into the small, shallow craters, looking for clues to what caused them, for though a good many selenologists believe they could have been made only by impact, a few vulcanists have speculated that some of the small craters might be what they call dimple craters—the result of the slumping of the surface into a underground cavity—and if this should be the case with a crater that the astronauts were inspecting, they would notice that it had a rounder and deeper bottom than that of an impact crater, like the dimple in the sand of a just turned hourglass. The rocks like fieldstones littering the *mare* in front of them may be sufficiently numerous so that the astronauts will have to exercise care not to trip; Dr. Dietrich describes parts of the moon as good ankle-breaking territory, but adds that it would be almost impossible for an astronaut to break an ankle, because he would fall with only a sixth of his normal weight. The astronauts will have no trouble seeing the rocks, for the early-morning sun picks them out as brilliantly as it does the westerly rims of the craters; the rocks catch the sun brightly on one side and cast long shadows from the other. Some of the rocks may be lighter than the blackish *mare* anyway, for they may be of a different material. However the larger craters were formed, the rocks were ejected from them in the process, and some of the rocks in front of the astronauts may have come from quite far away, for in low gravity explosions can send debris enormous distances. The rocks in front of the astronauts could have come from anywhere on the moon. This possibility is by no means farfetched, as the rays of the crater Tycho, which are probably lines of dust that were spattered during its formation, are thought by some selenologists to circle the moon entirely, a possibility that has inspired Dr. Urey to come up with an ingenious suggestion concerning a couple of the rays. Unlike the rest, these rays appear not to emanate from the crater's center, but to be tangential to it. Dr. Urey believes that these two rays are dust ejected during the impact that made Tycho; that the debris sprayed completely around the moon and back to Tycho; and that the amount by which the rays are offset from the crater's center represents the distance the moon rotated on its axis during a hundred and eighty minutes, which is the time that Dr. Urey calculates the trip took. (Vulcanists who find this theory hard to swallow point out that there are a number of other craters with offset rays, and that as the rays are offset differently in each case, the moon must have shifted around on its axis in a most erratic manner. These vulcanists evidently think that Dr. Urey is doing the same sort of thing as the astronomer in "Gulliver's Travels" who put a sundial on top of a weather vane, thinking that the revolutions of the earth matched the accidental turnings by the wind.)

Though some of the debris in front of the astronauts may have come from Tycho, about a thousand miles to the southeast, there is no immediate way for them, or the scientists on earth, to *know* where it came from. The procedure for taking a sample is first to describe the rock by radio to Dr. Dietrich—or whatever geologist is on duty at Houston—taking a guess as to its composition. (Since the photographs from the Surveyors indicate that basalt is the basic rock of the *maria*, most of the rocks that the astronauts undertake to describe will probably be basaltic.) Then they will note whether the rock is sharp and angular or rounded and smooth—for Surveyors have photographed both kinds. They will probably have a good deal to say about almost any rock, for selenologists become eloquent when presented with anything from the moon. Recently, one NASA geologist described a Surveyor photograph of a half-buried, rather ordinary-looking stone as follows: "Subangular in shape, with facets slightly rounded at the edges and corners. The lighter colored part of the rock is the more resistant to erosion, and therefore distinctive. Granularity of the block is not evident, but it shows mottling. Intersecting fracture planes resemble cleavage planes produced during static flow of rock under high shock pressure. The edges of the fractures also exhibit a rounding . . . " One of the most important observations that the astronauts will make is whether the dirt around the rock appears freshly scarred, the way it would if someone had just tossed a heavy stone onto a beach, or whether the rock is embedded in the ground with the soil packed tightly around it. Photographs have shown both situations, and some selenologists are perplexed by the embedded rocks, for there is no weathering or erosion on the moon to pack the soil around the rocks. Mr. Gold thinks the answer lies in his theory of electrostatic transportation, which he insists has filled up so many craters on the *maria* floors. It has simply filled up the ground broken by hurtling rocks as well, he says. Mr. Gold likes to talk about his particles as if they were water flowing downhill, swamping craters and surging like mud around the rocks. Dr. Shoemaker says that Mr. Gold's theory would lead you to expect to find puddles of dust in a great many depressions, and you don't find any such thing. Mr. Gold says you *do*. A good look by an astronaut at what has filled the broken ground around a rock might settle matters. Dr. Dietrich, not a dust man himself, doesn't dismiss Mr. Gold's theory out of hand, for he points out that, electrostatic field or no, *something* seems to have shifted the fine particles on the moon. (The something that did it might equally well have been the continuous shock of meteoric impacts or of volcanic quakes, which might have jolted the particles across the moon like sand jiggling on a sifter—or even a flood of actual water, which Dr. Urey has suggested may once have covered much of the moon.) But if Dr. Dietrich doesn't dismiss Mr. Gold's electrostatic theory, he doesn't embrace it very warmly, either. "Whenever Mr. Gold or Dr. Urey makes a noise, the rest of us *have* to look into it," Dr. Dietrich says, in exasperation. Looking into it isn't always easy, for both Mr. Gold's moon and Dr. Urey's moon are a good deal more mysterious than Dr. Dietrich's. By and large, the Surveyors have not been good to Mr. Gold, for in addition to not obligingly disappearing altogether into the surface of the moon, they have so far failed to turn up any evidence of electrostatic transportation of particles. Mr. Gold explains the latter failure by suggesting that the process may be going on at an extremely slow rate. "I don't expect to find a perpetual snowstorm up there," he says. Nevertheless, he would clearly like it if the astronauts did.

While one astronaut is noting the size, shape, and composition of the rock, possibly through a blizzard of tiny particles, the other will be snapping photographs of it with a Hasselblad, a camera similar to the one used by the astronauts aboard the Apollo 8 capsule last December. The Hasselblad has been designed expressly for taking snapshots on the moon, and, like all the other moon equipment, it is simple and foolproof. The astronauts may be tired—they will certainly be under considerable strain—and their hands could be a little shaky. Consequently, the astronaut will hold the camera by a grip very much like a pistol's. He won't have to change the film very often, for there are about one hundred and eighty exposures on a roll. (The film, a thin, lightweight variety developed specially for NASA because contrast between light and dark is greater on the moon than it is on the earth, will give pictures of much better resolution than televised ones.) He will have to set the camera for speed, range, and light; he will have no light meter, but he will have been given a rough idea beforehand of what the correct settings on the moon should be, given the angle of the sun. The control knobs are very big, so that he can set the camera while wearing his thick, clumsy gloves. Awkward as photography in a space suit may be, the astronaut will be a better photographer than any of the Surveyors on the moon, if only because he can look around and decide what to take and—equally important—what angle to take it from. He will face the rock under consideration, making sure that the sun is well to one side of him. It will be hard to take a picture into the blazing sun, and equally hard to take one directly away from the sun, not only because the astronaut would then be photographing his own shadow (a long one, since the sun is low on the horizon), but also because he has to avoid an effect called backscattering—a tendency for sunlight to be reflected from the surface of the moon. Backscattering can be almost blinding; many of the Surveyor photographs that were taken away from the sun—or "downsun," as Schmitt calls it—have been washed out by it. Rocks downsun are particularly likely to glint with backscattering, because they are apt to stick up perpendicularly from the flat *mare* and be hit head-on by the slanting early-morning sun. One explanation for backscattering could be that the moon and the rocks are indeed covered with a thin coat of powder as Mr. Gold says; if the grains are the way Mr. Gold thinks they are, sunlight would bounce back from them. To date, this peculiar lighting effect of the moon's surface is one of the strongest arguments in favor of Mr. Gold's powder. The astronaut, then, will face the rock in such a way that as much of it as possible is in sunlight *without* backscattering, for he has to avoid shadows; anything in shadow is hard to see on the moon because there is virtually no atmosphere to diffuse light. When he has found the rock's best profile, and is ready to shoot the picture, he won't raise the camera up to his eyes, because his space suit is tight at the shoulders. At one stage in its development, the Hasselblad had as a viewer a wire frame on top, like the old-fashioned Speed Graphics that newsmen used to carry had; however, the astronauts can't even raise their arms high enough to see through a wire frame on the camera's top. The camera has no viewer at all, and the astronaut will shoot from the hip—pistol-fashion, in accordance with the grip it has. The camera is squared off, like an old Brownie box camera, so the astronaut will have a close enough idea of where he is aiming. At first, the camera was to have had an extra-wide-angle lens, so that even if the astronaut's aim was off he would be sure to hit something; however, the astronaut's aim during practice has been so good that the wide-angle lens was dropped. When everything is ready, the astronaut will release the trigger. The trigger, which is built into the grip, is pulled exactly like that on a pistol. After the astronaut pulls the trigger, an electrical motor inside the camera winds the film to the next frame and cocks the trigger for the next shot, thus automatically preventing any double exposures.

While the photography is going on, the other astronaut, who has the tools, will be getting ready to knock a few chips off the rock to bring back to Dr. Dietrich and the other geologists. If the astronauts are to bring back a representative selection of samples, they won't have room for entire boulders. Aside from the fact that it is white, the hammer that the astronaut will be wielding will be little different from the slender hammers that geologists use; that is, it will have a long handle and an attenuated head with a chisel on one end. Though it has been found that the design of the geologist's hammer cannot be improved upon, that doesn't mean the human-factors engineers haven't tried. In a glass case at the Manned Spacecraft Center, there is an exhibition of human-factoring that includes three different hammers, along with graphs demonstrating how the force of impact is carried along the hammers' handles assuming that the hammers are in low gravity. The engineers did their low-gravity hammering in an airplane that was flying a series of roller-coaster-style parabolas, which put the plane and its contents at low gravity for about thirty seconds during each dive. Human-factors engineers took the trip with them, and although the engineers admit to having felt wobbly afterward, they nevertheless managed to come up with some useful tips for the astronauts. When the astronaut, who will be standing with his knees slightly bent but will otherwise be erect (he cannot bend at the waist), strikes the rock with the hammer, he won't swing the hammer with his whole arm, for in low gravity every action of the body has a more severe reaction than it would on earth; and in the case of the hammer thus might lift the astronaut straight up off the ground. Instead, he will use his wrist, hitting the rock a series of sharp taps. The taps won't be hard ones, for the hammer will have a greater tendency to rebound than it would on earth, and the back of the hammer, being a chisel, might puncture the suit. When the astronaut has gently knocked off a few chips, he will pick them up with the tongs by squeezing a trigger on the handle, which will cause a pair of wire hands at the far end to clench around the chips. If the chips are big ones, he may brush them clean and scratch a catalogue number on them with his combination tool, and then put them in one or more of the Teflon bags which have catalogue numbers already printed on them. (The two hundred Teflon bags—they are amber—will be in a small box that sits on top of the tool rack and looks like a napkin dispenser.) Next he will radio the catalogue number back to Houston, and then he will drop the sample into the big sack suspended in the center of the tool carrier. Finally, the other astronaut, who has been standing by with the camera, will take a closeup of the place where the sample had been, in order to give the geologists a complete picture of the sample's relationship to the terrain.

The astronauts' path toward the crater field will zigzag this way and that as they move from one item that catches their eye to another, avoiding craters the whole time. The astronauts will doubtless get sidetracked. Even Dr. Dietrich gets sidetracked without ever leaving the M.S.C., because there are a number of tempting craters that show up on his photograph. On the route he has picked out, he isn't even sure that he wouldn't go to the big crater *first* and the crater field *second,* on the ground that the big crater is the more spectacular of the two and he wouldn't want to miss it in the event that the trip had to be curtailed. Putting first things first is the most basic principle of the men who are planning the astronauts' stay on the moon. The astronauts could very well change plans in midstream, for exactly where they go is ultimately up to them. At one point, there was some thought that geologists back at the M.S.C. might guide the astronauts over television, telling them what to do, but this plan was vetoed by the astronauts almost before it was proposed. Dr. Elbert King, Curator of the Lunar Receiving Laboratory, who has had a hand in training the astronauts in geology, says, "Anyone who knows the astronauts knows that one thing they are not is robots who can be operated by remote control. They have every intention of making their own decisions while they are on the moon." Dr. King is more of an administrator than Dr. Dietrich, who gives the impression of being more of a geologist's geologist. Since Dr. King won't be able to follow the astronauts over television, he has done the next best thing; the astronauts will try to keep up a steady line of chatter to the scientists at the M.S.C. Dr. King says, "We want them to look with their mouths open. We tell them, 'Talk! Describe! Tell us what you see!' The tiniest observation might be crucial. Even if they don't know what something is, we want them to tell us what they *think* it is. 'Free associate' we tell them. I want to hear things like 'I wonder what that little pink rock is. It looks like it came from that crater over there.' The Apollo astronauts won't be tongue-tied, like some of the Mercury boys; we've seen to that. They'll have the background and the experience. Also, they'll have something to talk *about*. They have the fantastic responsibility of making these incredible observations." Dr. Dietrich and other geologists have already trained the astronauts to loosen their tongues by flying them to places they have never been before and sending them off with instructions to keep talking into microphones, even if they can't think of anything to say. All the places have been as moonlike as possible, such as the Valley of Ten Thousand Smokes, in Alaska, and Meteor Crater, in Arizona. "On some field trips, I'd be sitting behind a rock out there, listening over the radio to what they were saying," Dr. King recalls. "We'd record their comments on tape, and later on I'd critique what they'd said. If the astronaut missed mentioning a rock I knew was there, I'd light into him afterward, just like a football coach critiquing a fumble on a film of a game."

When the astronauts get to the crater field, they will probably talk a little faster, as if they were afraid to miss any rock that Dr. Dietrich might somehow have planted there, for the conglomeration of small craters will be the nearest thing to scenery they have seen yet. The astronaut with the camera will take a good many snapshots. If most of the *mare* is like a smooth black lake with a few raindrops falling into it, then the crater field is like a lake in a hailstorm. The astronauts will have to be careful as they maneuver among the craters, because the craters are so close together that where the rims brush, high crests have been thrown up, forming choppy waves; some craters actually intersect, like the rings in water during a heavy rainfall. Dr. Dietrich, who is closely bound to the soil in his thinking, describes the crater field as being typical badlands topography, pitted as if someone had been firing a shotgun into the sand. This may not be far from the mark, for he believes the crater field may have been caused by rubble shot out of a much bigger crater when it was formed. Secondary craters, as craters made in this way are called, are quite common on the moon. Normally, they form a pitted area around the primary, or parent, crater, though in the case of a really big primary, the secondaries may be scattered some distance away. Dr. Shoemaker, who has spent a good deal of time counting secondary craters around different primaries, measuring them, and plotting them on graphs (even selenology has its tedious aspects), says that a good-sized primary crater is apt to father a hundred thousand secondaries, the biggest of which is apt to be one-twentieth the diameter of the primary. Secondary craters are often smoother and rounder than primaries, which are usually flat-bottomed and can sometimes have quite jagged walls. To learn more about how primary craters spatter hosts of secondaries around them, some selenologists, among them Dr. Shoemaker, have studied craters left by atomic explosions whose force is thought to have been similar to that of the shocks causing craters on the moon. At the American Geophysical Union convention this spring, there was a film of an atomic explosion on the Yucca Flat, Nevada, showing, first, the flat, sandy ground with an occasional cactus sticking from it; then the ground slowly billowing up; then a shattering spray of earth and rocks as the explosion breached; and finally, from the air, the vast primary crater, a deep brown hole in the desert, surrounded by a host of secondary craters, thinning out like spray as they got farther away. It was found that the secondary craters in the Yucca Flat are not always perfectly round, because the rocks that made them, having been lobbed from the primary crater, were not traveling fast enough to generate a high-velocity-impact explosion, the way meteors do. In many cases, the rocks that made the secondary craters are still be be found inside them. Dr. Dietrich wants the astronauts to retrieve samples of such rocks from inside the moon's secondary craters, because the presumption is that the farther a rock has flown from a primary crater, the deeper underground it started from. The rocks that made secondary craters in the crater field may have come from very deep underground, because the primary crater in this case is so far away that Dr. Dietrich doesn't know where it is.

When the secondary craters have been robbed of their rocks, like eggs from nests, the astronauts will start back toward the LM by way of the big crater. They will have been gone from the LM for about an hour and they may well be getting exhausted. NASA is looking into ways the astronauts can cover more ground with less effort, and accordingly the Grumman Aircraft Engineering Corporation has been working on a moon car called the Lunar Module/Lunar Roving Vehicle and which the company abbreviates LM/LRV, like an advertisement for a popular cigarette. The car can travel as fast as twenty miles an hour, and thus increase the amount of terrain an astronaut can explore about a hundredfold. Nothing about the moon car looks as if it came from Detroit or anywhere on earth. A special car is needed on the moon because a conventional automobile is far too heavy to send economically, and even if one could be got up there, the engine wouldn't start, because gasoline engines need air. Also, the tires would explode, because the moon is in an almost perfect vacuum. And even if these difficulties could be got around, driving a Detroit model on the moon would be exceptionally hazardous, because, in the moon's one-sixth gravity, cars would bounce a good deal farther than they do here. For instance, if a jeep going ten miles an hour were to hit a four-inch bump on the moon, it would bounce twenty feet. It would also be six times as likely to turn over. Unlike a Detroit car, the LM/LRV can be economically taken to the moon, for it weighs on earth only some seven hundred pounds, without an astronaut, and can be folded to fit into one of the lunar module's storage bays. It runs on electricity, so the absence of air presents no difficulty. It is a wide, low-slung machine that looks like a buckboard—all but the wheels. To get around the bouncing problem, the designers had to invent a new kind of wheel, which would contain the force of any bounce within the wheel itself without transmitting it to the car. The wheels, which are called metalastic wheels, have to be elastic so that when they hit a bump on the moon their shape will be distorted, with the rims almost touching the hubs; in distorting, the wheels absorb the shock while the rest of the car continues on a level course. They are large white cones, with the open ends facing outward, resembling radar dishes except that they have wide metal treads around their rims. When the astronaut drives the car, which is not much more than a white metal frame, he will sit on a low seat in front of the forward axle and extend his legs ahead of him until his feet fit into a couple of stirrups at the ends of metal bars. Next, he puts his arms firmly on armrests, which steady his hands against any jouncing of the rest of his body; otherwise the car, which is operated by the astronaut's right hand, will skitter out of control. The car operates by a sort of stick system which is steering wheel, clutch, brake, and accelerator rolled into one. The astronaut puts his right hand on a pistol-like grip; if he moves his hand forward, the car goes ahead, and if he moves it to one side, the car turns. On earth, the car would take off with an electrical whir and the metalastic wheels would squeak like the leather in a new pair of shoes; but on the moon, the drive will be silent. As the car picks up speed, the wheels stretch out of shape, coming to a point at the top. (This distortion is one of the ways they dissipate jolts.) Smashing into a rock will punch the wheels completely out of shape as though for an instant the car were riding on squashy melon rinds; however, car and driver continue on a level plane, unruffled. Lunar dust will shower outwards from the wheels as the car churns across the moon, the treads on the wheels leaving a trail like tank tracks on the *mare.*

As the astronauts walk (not ride) along, the ground under their feet may be a little crunchy, for in addition to being sandy, dusty, or powdery (as it has been variously described), it may be pebbly as well, some of the larger pebbles appearing to be aggregates of smaller ones, so that the astronauts may feel that they are taking a walk on a heap of clinkers. They will have to keep their eyes open for evidence of crevasses underlying the *mare.* Crevasses—or rilles, as the selenologists call them—are plentiful in the *maria,* and even though all the Apollo landing sites have been chosen partly to avoid them, it isn't impossible that these crevasses may extend under the surface, lightly hidden by Mr. Gold's ubiquitous powder. Mr. Gold has suggested that the astronauts should be roped together like mountaineers, for one of them could tumble into a rille the same way an unwary mountain climber falls into a crevasse that has been lightly bridged by snow—and, like snow, the powder may be slippery. In spite of the danger of hidden rilles, the astronauts have refused to be roped together. If they come across a rille, they will be eager to take samples around it, taking care not to fall in, for rilles and what caused them are the trench warfare in the battle among different groups of selenologists. The vulcanists maintain that some meandering rilles—called sinuous rilles—are caused by underground volcanic fissures from which the magma has drained, so that the surface above it has caved in, forming a long winding trench. On the other hand, Mr. Gold and Dr. Urey, who believe that there may be water beneath the moon's surface, have an alternative, non-volcanic, explanation—that these rilles are evidence of meandering underground rivers that undermine the ground, making it collapse along the course of the river. The question of the rilles gets as murky as most other matters pertaining to the moon. There are long rows of craters like strings of water droplets, which vulcanists say are evidence of subterranean fissures that have caved in here and there. The impact men say that these crater rows are obviously caused by meteors that fractured before hitting the moon—that the fragments sprayed out to form the line of craters, much as a handful of pebbles hitting the water will form a string of ripples.

By the time the astronauts got halfway to the big crater, they would perhaps be feeling totally lost, adrift in a never-ending sea of craters, if it weren't for the LM, squatting like a strange shiny lunar insect three-quarters of a kilometre away. Even if the LM were out of sight over the nearby lunar horizon, they could always follow their own tracks back to it, for their footprints, perhaps a quarter of an inch deep, may be noticeably blacker than the surrounding *mare;* the ground may darken below the surface. Their trail will be a winding one, threading its way among the millions of craters like rabbit tracks through a particularly thick woods. Wherever the astronauts brush by a crater, the track will be a blackish smudge, for they will pause and look into each sizable crater they come upon as if it were the only crater on the moon. One job they will try to do is to get samples of dirt from around as great a range of craters as they can, No. 1 through No. 8 on the scale of age and sharpness, to see if there is any difference in the material around them, and particularly in its color. The color differences will be only in shades of gray. Later, geologists would like to make a graph coordinating the sharpness of craters with the color of the material around them. Some geologists think that the blackish soil of the *maria* has been darkened through time by a bombardment of protons from space, so that if there is a correlation between the sharpness of a crater and its color, and if it can be shown that its sharpness has to do with its age, it may be possible to determine the relative age of craters and other features of the moon just by looking at their color, possibly from the earth, through a telescope. If Dr. Dietrich were near the radio, and if the astronauts asked his advice, he might urge them to be sure to get a sample from any small No. 8's they happen across, for the sharpest craters, if they are indeed the newest, would be the least affected by proton darkening, and thus the material around them would be closest to its original form. Being in a vacuum will have made the dust sticky. As the astronauts move about, they may find that their white space suits get quite dirty, and stay dirty, for lunar grit is hard to get off. In the spring of 1967, NASA made one of the Surveyors hop about twenty feet by briefly restarting its rocket, and dust that had settled on it remained there, as if it were New York City grit.

As the astronauts dip into small craters to scoop out blackish powder, many of the principal investigators—the scientists who will have first crack at analyzing the samples after they are brought back, sorted, and released from quarantine—will be listening eagerly at the M.S.C. for hints about the nature of the material being collected. About four days later, the rock boxes, containing sixty-five pounds of moon, will arrive at the Lunar Receiving Laboratory, in Houston. Each box will be wrapped in a couple of large Teflon bags to seal off any organisms that might have attached themselves to the outsides of the boxes while they were on the moon. The boxes are opened inside a small round metal chamber, whose interior pressure is kept at a near vacuum, similar to the pressure on the moon, but before they get there they first have to pass through a series of three compartments where the boxes are taken out of the Teflon bags and are scrubbed with nitrogen to remove any earthly organism that might have gotten onto the boxes after they returned from the moon. Technicians on the outside can reach into the three compartments by means of rubber gloves set into the compartments' sides, and into the vacuum chamber with a pair of beefed-up space suit gloves that have been set into the side of the chamber. The gloves are hard to manipulate because they protrude rigidly inwards, fingers extended stiffly, for the vacuum lets the earth's atmospheric pressure on the outside inflate the gloves like balloons. The chamber is necessary because (among other reasons) some scientists feel that there is a possibility of fine particles of moon dust exploding if exposed to the oxygen in the earth's atmosphere; as the oxygen in the moon's rare atmosphere is a negligible quantity (if indeed there is any oxygen there at all), moon dust exposed to the earth's atmosphere might oxidize rapidly, exploding even, and Dr. King doesn't want to run the risk of having any samples annihilate themselves like gunpowder. When a box is finally in the vacuum chamber and rid of any earthly material that could contaminate the samples, a technician will reach into the chamber through the gloves, throw back the bolt on the front of the box, undo the straps on top, open the lid, and gingerly lift out the small Teflon bags like a jeweller emptying sacks of diamonds from a briefcase. Dr. King will get his first good look at the samples a little later, when they are lifted up a short elevator to sit on a turntable, where they will be photographed from six different angles and where Dr. King will make certain preliminary decisions about their disposition. Portions of the samples will be shunted down a longer pipe into Dr. Kemmerer's laboratory, a floor below—a Noah's Ark of sorts, in which representative forms of earthly life are to be exposed to them. Others will be dispatched to an underground laboratory to be measured for radioactivity. Clearly, nobody is taking any chances; if any of the moon material was planted there as a message from a higher civilization, such as the mysterious humming slab in the film "2001," now is when the message will be discovered. Most of the samples will stay in the main chamber until the quarantine is lifted. By this time, the vacuum chamber will look like the assembly line in an Amsterdam diamond-cutting factory. Like large diamonds, some of the larger samples will be broken down so that there will be more to go around. Then the samples will be packed in special containers for shipment to a hundred and forty experimenters who will be studying them. Not all the samples will be distributed right away, though; NASA plans to hold some back for what it calls "second-generation experiments," and these samples will be handed out later. "You always seem to have your best ideas on what to do with a sample after you've used it all up, so we are making sure this won't happen," Dr. King has explained. About ten per cent of the sample material, moreover, will stay permanently in vacuum storage at the L.R.L., against the possibility that new techniques of scientific analysis will be developed in the future. However, most of the experimenters seem to have a pretty good idea about what they will do with their samples right now. Mr. Gold, who is to get one, says he will make (among other things) the same measurements that he and others have already made through telescopes (such as infrared measurements and measurements by polaroid light), the idea being to confirm the accuracy of telescopic techniques, so that they can be extended with confidence to other areas of the moon. Mr. Gold will, of course, be interested in any dust the astronauts bring back. Some of the experimenters will have spent years perfecting new techniques of analysis for their samples. Another selenologist, Dr. Paul Gast, a geochemist at Lamont-Doherty, has headed a team that has spent what he calls "several man-years" figuring out the best way to handle the one or two grams of moon he expects to get. He hopes to get a piece of igneous rock (it is by no means certain that he will), which he can analyze in order to establish how long ago it passed from the molten to the solid state. In doing this, he will have to look for as many as thirty different elements. "On earth, you never analyze one small sample for that many elements. Usually, when you've worked with a sample once or twice, you throw it away and get another one," he says. He won't be able to be so cavalier with the half gram of moon at his disposal. The work has to be planned with great care, because often the test for one element can ruin the sample for other anaylses.

Some of the samples will be tested for any gasses they may contain, and Dr. King says that one gas-isotope the experimenters will be particularly interested in testing for is Xenon 129, which has been found in the rock of a good many meteors. Xenon 129 was very abundant during the infancy of the solar system, and meteors that contain it are therefore thought to be older than the earth, which has a negligible amount of Xenon 129. If the experimenters should turn up a substantial quantity of the isotope in the lunar samples, the inference would be that the moon, too, is older than the earth.

As the astronauts prospect along, stopping here and there to knock off a rock chip that may keep a scientist back on earth occupied for years, they will be getting closer to the big crater, which is only half a kilometre from the LM. In Dr. Dietrich's Orbiter photograph of the site, the crater is a pockmark that registers about No. 5 on the scale of age and sharpness. It is two hundred metres across. As the astronauts approach it, they will come upon increasing amounts of rubble, spewed from the crater during its formation. The astronauts will have to watch their step to avoid tripping, but actually they will be walking too slowly to trip, because Dr. Dietrich would like them to sample the debris at intervals as they walk toward the crater, for the rubble from a crater represents a cross-section of the rock underlying the *maria*. The more distant debris will have come from deep down and the rubble on the raised lip from higher up, so walking toward a crater will be like climbing the substrata of the *mare*. The first debris that the astronauts will come to will have come from a depth equal to up to one-fourth the diameter of the crater—from fifty metres down, that is, or a good distance below the present floor of the crater. The astronauts will go no farther than the top of the crater's rim—a jumble of rocks like a tumble-down circular stone wall. It would be comparatively hard to do so, since the inside wall of the crater, a rocky scree, slopes quite sharply to the flat crater floor, thirty or forty metres below. (Theoretically, slopes on the moon can be precipitous, for the angle at which a rock will remain in place on a hillside is a good deal greater in low gravity than on earth.) The astronauts will probably be eager to go down, for the crater's sides may be layered in the way the walls of some quarries are on earth, providing an even better cross-section than the rubble outside the crater. It would be interesting to know whether the *maria* were built up by successive flows of lava, or whether they were loose dust a long way down. (If they should go into the crater, they would probably find the loose, dusty material extending at least part way down, for many selenologists think the powdery stuff is quite deep. Mr. Gault, who likes to get down to the grit as much as Dr. Shoemaker does, has fired pellets at high speeds into tubs filled with fine-grained sands—an experiment that sounds as if it might have been done at the Grand Academy of Lagado—and has found that the resulting craters look very much like the ones on the moon. A rim on a crater is an almost certain sign that the crater is in loose material, for Mr. Gault has found that when he fires his pellets into a solid surface, the pellet leaves no rim at all—just a hole.) However, the astronauts won't go down; they are prohibited from going into big craters, because if they did so they would be out of sight of the LM, and therefore they would lose radio contact with Houston—and also with each other. Besides, the interior of a large crater is a good deal hotter than the surrounding *maria,* because the sun's rays bounce back and forth inside it. A crater could be like an oven. Another danger is the possibility of sinking into a morass of Mr. Gold's dust, which, under some circumstances, might settle deeply into the bottoms of craters. In "Earthlight," which Clarke wrote in 1955, when Mr. Gold's dust theories were more attractive than they are today, two of Clarke's astronauts tumble into what he calls a dust bowl while they are driving across the moon in a sort of Land Rover. The dust in the crater is so fine that "it begins to flow like a liquid and accumulates at the bottom of the crater," Clarke writes. "In almost all respects, indeed, it *is* a liquid: it is so incredibly fine that if collected in a bucket, it will slop around like a rather mobile oil." Clarke's astronauts flounder perilously in this unpleasant soup, but it is not thought likely that the Apollo astronauts will encounter the same fate, particularly if they keep out of craters.

Standing safely at the crater's edge, the astronauts will probably click away with their camera, undoubtedly taking more pictures than they need. Some craters are spectacular. Copernicus, for instance, is a saucer fifty-five miles broad and two to three miles deep, or three times as deep as the Grand Canyon. (Dr. Dietrich would give a great deal for debris from Copernicus, which might come from nine miles down.) A photograph of Copernicus that was taken by an Orbiter satellite skimming over the rim is spectacular. The inner walls of Copernicus cascade in a series of concentric steps, the risers cliffs a mile high, to a flat floor, pocked here and there with smaller craters; the central peak is a mountain about two thousand feet high. Although the crater on whose rim the astronauts will be standing is no Copernicus, it is awesome enough, being a hole whose diameter is the same as a long city block. As with Copernicus, the dish of the crater isn't smooth, like a saucer, but, rather, appears to descend in at least two big concentric steps. On earth, craters with stepped walls are usually volcanic collapse calderas—formations that collapsed over a period of time. The magma beneath drained away little by little, so that the crater caved in in successive stages instead of all at once. (Some impact men, who have no intention of ceding Copernicus, or any other terraced crater, to the vulcanists, claim that such craters are made by meteors impacting into layered ground, the resistance of the different layers accounting for the terraces in the crater walls.) Dr. Dietrich is one of those who would like to claim Copernicus, a spectacular prize, for the vulcanists. He confesses, "I spent fifteen years as a volcanic geologist before I came to NASA, and so I tend to see volcanic features wherever I look." He won't venture to guess whether the crater that the astronauts are looking at is volcanic or not; that is for the astronauts to say. Dr. Dietrich says that their minds will be as open as anyone's mind could be, for they will have been trained by both volcanic and impact geologists. The astronauts can't help having ideas of their own, however, he says, and he adds, "If Schmitt is up there, all bets are off, because he's a professional geologist." The geologists at the M.S.C. who, like Dietrich, tend to be vulcanists, regard Schmitt with some suspicion, for he worked for the United States Geological Survey, which Dietrich regards as having been a hotbed of meteor men. (In fact, Dr. Masursky, the chief of the Geological Survey's astrogeological branch, has recently trumped Dr. Dietrich's Copernicus by claiming Tycho for the impact selenologists.) There was once talk around NASA that a professional geologist should not be sent on one of the early missions, lest his bias interfere with his judgment. This argument infuriates Dietrich and Schmitt alike, because they both believe that a man's bias gives him a frame of reference that is essential in observing. Schmitt, who doesn't think of himself as either an impact man or a vulcanist, is especially indignant. "When a man knows what to look for, his value snowballs," he says. Schmitt believes the value of his own presence on the moon would decidedly snowball, because he feels that he knows enough so that once he is there, he could tell fairly quickly whether a crater was formed by an impacting meteor or a collapsing caldera. "Given a new crater, I would have a reasonable chance of spotting how it was formed right off," he says. "There are small geological differences between volcanic and impact craters, such as the distribution of rock around them or the character of the glass in their vicinity. Any geologist might be able to tell the difference. But he'd have to be there first."

When the astronauts have finished poking around the rim of the crater, they will trudge back to the LM. At this point, Dr. Dietrich likes to imagine that they will turn to the geologists back in Houston, to ask whether the earthbound scientists have any special requests. The astronauts will have been consulting the geologists all along, and they may have thrown in such suggestions as "Try to get a sample of rock from a secondary crater," but they will not have intruded much beyond that. However, the M.S.C. geologists will have been following the astronauts' path closely on a blowup of the Orbiter photograph, so that if they are asked to make a specific request, they will have no difficulty coming up with one. Dr. Dietrich has already picked out a couple of smaller craters that he would like them to look at if they have time.

On the field trip, the chances are that the astronauts will have collected more material than they will have room for. When they get back to the LM, they will have to decide what to leave behind. All the equipment used on the moon, including the tools, the tool rack, and the entire ALSEP, will be left behind on the moon; even so, there is room for no more than sixty-five pounds of samples, the maximum amount of baggage the LM can carry and still rendezvous with the Apollo command module. The astronauts will have a problem deciding what to throw away among the field-trip samples, which are still in the sack inside the tool carrier. They will do the sorting on the fold-out table that they set up before. Their small weighing scale, which is a little like the pocket scales fishermen use, has been resting unused in the tool carrier all this time; now they will hang it from the LM's ladder, and then they may hang the sack from that, removing samples until the weight is down to sixty-five pounds (or, on the moon, slightly under eleven pounds). Their problem is essentially that of a man who is packing for an airplane flight and has to decide what to leave behind so that his suitcase won't be overweight. Doubtless the interplanetary airwaves will be ringing with questions like "Shall we ditch the vesiculated basalt or the little pink rock?" or "We don't need this powdery stuff, do we?" Hard as these decisions may be, they may not make that much difference. Dr. Dietrich says, "Anything they bring back from the moon will be of interest," and he adds cautiously, "Whatever they bring back on the first few missions probably won't settle too many major questions. At the beginning, we'll probably find every theory substantiated. It has happened that way right along, as with Mr. Gold and his dust theories. But we will have *begun* to accumulate data. We might *begin* to get somewhere."

After the astronauts have packed the samples they will take back with them, they will close the lid of each rock box and clamp four steel straps across the top. As the straps are tightened, a sharp edge that has been set along the lip of the lid bites into a soft metal, indium, that covers the lip of the box, making a vacuum-tight seal. The insides of the boxes are heavily ribbed, so that when they are returned to earth, the pressure of the atmosphere will not crush them, destroying the scant lunar environment inside. Then, for good measure, they will turn a knob on the front, which throws a bolt into a socket. Next, the astronauts may make a little cache out of the equipment they are leaving behind, something like a cairn on an Arctic beach. Then they will hoist the rock boxes up into the LM with a rope, and after that they will climb the ladder, leaving the moon seemingly almost as empty as it was before they came. The moon, however, having had sixty-five pounds of its material replaced by perhaps more than two hundred pounds of experimental instruments and discarded equipment, will never be the same again. The experiments will be pumping information from deep in the center of the moon out through its ephemeral atmosphere, now somewhat more substantial with rocket pollution. Not the least of the changes will be the two sets of footsteps emanating from the artificial crater under the LM, which go first out to the ALSEP and back, and then farther out, threading amongst the craters in a thin circle that has about it something of the tenuous outer thrust of a ring in the water. The footprints will remain No. 8 on the scale of age and sharpness for some time.